First Edition

D1397414

Support Coach

TARGET ➤ **Foundational Mathematics 4**

GEORGIA

Dr. Jerry Kaplan
Senior Mathematics Consultant

Georgia Common Core Support Coach, Target: Foundational Mathematics, First Edition, Grade 4
T155GA   ISBN-13: 978-1-62362-295-4
Contributing Writers: Q2A/Bill Smith   **Cover Design:** Q2A/Bill Smith

Triumph Learning® 136 Madison Avenue, 7th Floor, New York, NY 10016

Contents

Multiplicative Comparisons

PLUG IN Multiplication and Division Facts

You can use repeated addition to help you find the **product**.

$$3 \times 5 = \boxed{15}$$
$$5 + 5 + 5 = 15$$

Think: 3 times 5 means "3 groups of 5."

You can use repeated subtraction to help you find the **quotient**.

$$15 \div 5 = \boxed{3}$$
$$15 - 5 = 10$$
$$10 - 5 = 5$$
$$5 - 5 = 0$$

Think: Subtract 5 each time until you reach 0.

A **fact family** shows how multiplication and division are related.

$$3 \times 5 = 15$$
$$5 \times 3 = 15$$
$$15 \div 3 = 5$$
$$15 \div 5 = 3$$

I see! Related facts use the same numbers.

Words to Know

product
the answer in a multiplication problem
$$2 \times 3 = 6$$

quotient
the answer in a division problem
$$6 \div 3 = 2$$

fact family
a set of related facts that use the same numbers
$$2 \times 3 = 6 \quad 6 \div 2 = 3$$
$$3 \times 2 = 6 \quad 6 \div 3 = 2$$

 What would happen to the product if you made 5 groups of 3 squares?

A You can use repeated addition to find the product.

 Multiply. $4 \times 5 = \square$

❶ Think about the number sentence.

❷ Add 5 four times.

❸ Find the product.

4×5 means ___**4**___ groups of _____.

_____ + _____ + _____ + _____ = _____

$4 \times 5 = $ _____

The number of times you subtract is the quotient.

B You can use repeated subtraction to find the quotient.

DO Divide. $16 \div 4 = \square$

1. Start with 16. Subtract 4 each time until you reach 0.

2. Count the number of times you subtracted.

3. Write the quotient.

____16____ − ____4____ = _____

_____ − _____ = _____

_____ − _____ = _____

_____ − _____ = _____

You subtracted 4 _____ times.

$16 \div 4 = $ _____

C You can use a related fact to help you find the quotient.

DO Divide. $21 \div 3 = \square$

1. Look at the numbers in the number sentence.

2. Write a related multiplication fact with 3 and 21.

3. Write the quotient.

The number sentence has the numbers ____21____ and _____.

Think: 3 times what number is 21?

$3 \times $ _____ $= 21$

$21 \div 3 = $ _____

PRACTICE

Use repeated addition or subtraction to find the product or quotient.

1 $6 \times 5 = $ _____

2 $36 \div 9 = $ _____

Use a related fact to find the quotient.

3 $40 \div 8 = $ _____

$8 \times $ _____ $= 40$

4 $27 \div 3 = $ _____

$3 \times $ _____ $= 27$

Multiplication as a Comparison

You can use multiplication to compare two numbers.

There is 1 group of 2 blue squares. There are 3 groups of 2 green squares.

There are 3 times as many green squares as blue squares.

$6 = 3 \times 2$

I see! 6 is 3 times as many as 2.

There are 2 blue squares and 6 green squares.

DISCUSS Use multiplication to compare the two numbers 4 and 12.

A You can compare numbers to show multiplication.

DO Compare the two sets of squares.

❶ Count the blue squares.

❷ Count the red squares.

❸ Complete the sentence to compare the two sets.

___1___ group of ___6___ blue squares

There are _____ blue squares.

_____ groups of _____ red squares

There are _____ red squares.

24 is _____ times as many as 6.

B You can write a multiplication sentence to compare numbers.

Multiply the number of groups by the number in each group.

DO   Write a multiplication sentence to represent the two sets of triangles.

❶ Count the yellow triangles and the purple triangles.

❷ Complete the sentence to compare the two sets.

❸ Write the multiplication sentence.

There are _____ yellow triangles.

There are _____ purple triangles.

8 is _____ times as many as 4.

_____ = _____ × _____

DISCUSS   Ashley said, "These pictures show that 9 is 3 times as many as 2." What can you tell Ashley about her statement?

PRACTICE

Write a multiplication sentence to represent the two sets of shapes.

❶

____1___ group of _____ blue squares. There are _____ blue squares.

_____ groups of _____ orange squares. There are _____ orange squares.

30 is _____ times as many as 5.

_____ = _____ × _____

Use the comparison to write a multiplication sentence.

❷ 27 is 3 times as many as 9.

_____ = _____ × _____

❸ 28 is 7 times as many as 4.

_____ = _____ × _____

Ava has 3 stickers. Kylie has 4 times as many stickers as Ava. How many stickers does Kylie have?

Write an **equation** to represent the problem.

Make a drawing to model the problem.

Use △ to stand for Kylie's stickers. Use 4 and 3 as **factors**.

△ is 4 times as many as 3.
△ = 4 × 3
△ = 12

Ava   Kylie

Kylie has 12 stickers.

Words to Know

equation
a number sentence with an equal sign (=)

$$4 \times 3 = \square$$
$$\square = 4 \times 3$$

factors
the numbers you multiply

$$3 \times 2 = 6$$
factors

DISCUSS Make a comparison word problem using the number sentence 4 × 4 = 16.

LESSON LINK

PLUG IN

There are many ways to find products and quotients.

$$2 \times 4 = 8$$
$$8 \div 4 = 2$$

POWER UP

Multiplication can compare two numbers.

6 is 3 times as many as 2
$$6 = 3 \times 2$$

GO!

I see! I can use multiplication to solve comparison problems.

Use □ to stand for Isa's cards.

WORK TOGETHER

Write an equation to solve. Use a Grouping Mat and draw counters to model the problem.

- The equation □ = 2 × 8 represents the problem.

- The top row shows Michael's cards. He has 8 cards.

- The bottom row shows Isa's cards. She has twice as many as 8.

Isa bought 16 cards.

Michael bought 8 cards. Isa bought twice as many cards as Michael. How many cards did Isa buy?

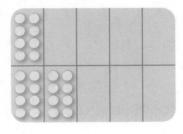

□ is twice as many as 8.

□ = 2 × 8

□ = 16

Grouping Mat can be found on p. 211.

A Use a Grouping Mat and draw counters to model the problem.

DO Write an equation and solve.
A small rug is 5 feet long. A big rug is 3 times as long as the small rug. How many feet long is the big rug?

1. Use a symbol to represent the number you need to find.

2. Write the equation.

3. Multiply and solve.

4. Model the problem.

Use △ to stand for _____.

△ is _____ times as long as _____ feet.

△ = _____ × _____

△ = _____

The big rug is _____ feet long.

DISCUSS Jerome said "14 is 6 times as many as 2." How can Jerome check his answer?

I can make a model.

PRACTICE

Make a drawing to model the problem.

1 James has 4 football cards. Benjamin has 5 times as many football cards as James. How many football cards does Benjamin have?

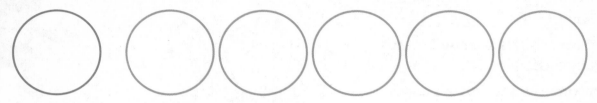

Benjamin has _____ football cards.

Write an equation to solve. Make a model to represent the problem.

> **Grouping Mat** can be found on p. 213.

2 Mrs. Walker has 4 boys in her karate class. There are 2 times as many girls as boys in the class. How many girls are in Mrs. Walker's karate class?

Use ☐ to stand for _____.

☐ is _____ times as many as __**4**__.

☐ = _____ × _____

☐ = _____

There are _____ girls in Mrs. Walker's karate class.

> **HINT**
> The number in one group is one of the factors.

3 Bella read 3 times as many pages as Morgan. Morgan read 8 pages. How many pages did Bella read?

Use △ to stand for _____.

△ is _____ times as many as _____.

△ = _____ × _____

△ = _____

Bella read _____ pages.

Write an equation to solve.

4 There are 6 green apples in a basket. There are 3 times as many red apples in the basket. How many red apples are in the basket?

☐ = _____ × _____

☐ = _____

The basket has _____ red apples.

5 A truck has 4 times as many wheels as a car. A car has 4 wheels. How many wheels does the truck have?

☐ = _____ × _____

☐ = _____

The truck has _____ wheels.

Solve.

6 Linda's bracelet is 6 inches long. She has a necklace that is 5 times as long as the bracelet. How many inches long is the necklace? _____

I can make a model to represent the problem.

7 The library is 5 miles from Gabriel's house. The art museum is 4 times as many miles away from Gabriel's house. How far is the art museum from Gabriel's house? _____

DISCUSS

See the Pattern

Jasmine completed some multiplication comparisons.

Find the missing numbers.

I can write number sentences to help me see the pattern.

__2__ is 2 times as many as 1.   _____ is 2 times as many as 4.

__4__ is 2 times as many as 2.   _____ is 2 times as many as 5.

_____ is 2 times as many as 3.   _____ is 2 times as many as 6.

What pattern do you see in these comparisons?

PROBLEM SOLVING

PLANTING TREES

READ

Mr. Garcia has 5 maple trees. He planted 7 times as many ash trees as maple trees. How many ash trees did Mr. Garcia plant?

PLAN

• What is the problem asking you to find?

You need to find the number of _____.

• What do you need to know to solve the problem?

Mr. Garcia has _____ maple trees.

He planted _____ times as many ash trees as maple trees.

• How can you compare the numbers?

You can write an equation and make a model.

SOLVE

Use △ to stand for _____.

△ is _____ times as many as _____.

△ = _____ × _____

△ = _____

CHECK

Make a model.

Mr. Garcia planted _____ ash trees.

I can make a model to check the answer.

PRACTICE

Use the problem-solving steps to help you.

1 The Pizza Shack sold 6 pizzas in one hour. The next hour they sold 5 times as many pizzas. How many pizzas did they sell during the second hour?

CHECKLIST
- [ ] READ
- [ ] PLAN
- [ ] SOLVE
- [ ] CHECK

2 Natalie ran 4 times as many miles in June as in May. She ran 9 miles in May. How many miles did Natalie run in June?

CHECKLIST
- [ ] READ
- [ ] PLAN
- [ ] SOLVE
- [ ] CHECK

3 Gavin sold peanuts and popcorn at a baseball game. He sold 8 bags of popcorn. He sold 2 times as many bags of peanuts as popcorn. How many bags of peanuts did Gavin sell?

CHECKLIST
- [ ] READ
- [ ] PLAN
- [ ] SOLVE
- [ ] CHECK

Multi-Step Word Problems

PLUG IN Adding and Subtracting Whole Numbers

To **add** or **subtract**, set up the problem vertically. Line up the digits with the same place value. Start with the ones column and **regroup** as needed.

Add 167 + 684.

Regroup to the column to the left.

$$\begin{array}{r} {\scriptstyle 1\ 1} \\ 1\,6\,7 \\ +\,6\,8\,4 \\ \hline 8\,5\,1 \end{array}$$

Subtract 754 − 138.

Regroup from the column to the left.

$$\begin{array}{r} {\scriptstyle 4\ 14} \\ 7\,\cancel{5}\,\cancel{4} \\ -\,1\,3\,8 \\ \hline 6\,1\,6 \end{array}$$

> 11 ones were regrouped as 1 ten 1 one. 15 tens were regrouped as 1 hundred 5 tens.

> 4 ones is not enough to subtract 8 ones. Regroup 1 ten as 10 ones from the 5 in 754.

Words to Know

add	**subtract**	**regroup**
to find the total when two or more values are joined	to find how many are left when a value is taken away	to rename a number a different way
100 + 25 = 125	100 − 25 = 75	13 ones = 1 ten 3 ones

DISCUSS When adding, when do you need to regroup?

A You can line up place values to add.

DO Add 248 + 135.

❶ Line up the digits with the same place value.

❷ Add the ones. Regroup.

❸ Add the tens.

❹ Add the hundreds.

$$\begin{array}{r} \square\ \\ 2\quad 4\quad 8 \\ +\ 1\quad 3\quad 5 \\ \hline \square\ \square\ \square \end{array}$$

B You can line up place values to subtract.

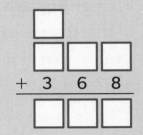

Regroup from the column to the left when needed.

DO   Subtract 538 − 368.

① Line up the numbers vertically by place value.

② Subtract the ones.

③ Subtract the tens. Regroup from the hundreds column.

④ Subtract the hundreds.

⑤ Use addition to check your answer.

$$\begin{array}{ccc} \square & \square & \\ \not{5} & \not{3} & 8 \\ - 3 & 6 & 8 \\ \hline \square & \square & \square \end{array}$$

$$\begin{array}{ccc} \square & & \\ \square & \square & \square \\ + 3 & 6 & 8 \\ \hline \square & \square & \square \end{array}$$

PRACTICE

Add.

1   499 + 267

$$\begin{array}{ccc} \square & \boxed{1} & \\ 4 & 9 & 9 \\ + 2 & 6 & 7 \\ \hline \square & \square & \square \end{array}$$

2   923 + 184

$$\begin{array}{cccc} \square & & & \\ & 9 & 2 & 3 \\ + & 1 & 8 & 4 \\ \hline \square & \square & \square & \square \end{array}$$

Subtract. Use addition to check.

3   862 − 361

$$\begin{array}{ccc} 8 & 6 & 2 \\ - 3 & 6 & 1 \\ \hline \square & \square & \square \end{array}$$

$$\begin{array}{ccc} \square & \square & \square \\ + 3 & 6 & 1 \\ \hline \square & \square & \square \end{array}$$

4   674 − 406

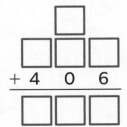

$$\begin{array}{ccc} \square & \square & \\ 6 & \not{7} & \not{4} \\ - 4 & 0 & 6 \\ \hline \square & \square & \boxed{8} \end{array}$$

$$\begin{array}{ccc} & \square & \\ \square & \square & \square \\ + 4 & 0 & 6 \\ \hline \square & \square & \square \end{array}$$

POWER UP Comparison Story Problems

Makayla found 4 seashells. Lily found twice as many seashells. How many seashells did Lily find?

Write an **equation**.

Lily has 2 times as many as 4.

Use *s* to stand for Lily's seashells.

$s = 2 \times 4$

$s = 8$

I can use any letter to represent Lily's seashells.

Make a drawing.

Use repeated addition to check.

$2 \times 4 \rightarrow 4 + 4 = 8$

Lily found 8 seashells.

 Words to Know

equation

a number sentence with an equal sign

$r = 5 \times 8$ $5 \times 8 = r$

DISCUSS What are some words that help you choose an operation when solving a word problem?

A You can use multiplication to solve comparison problems.

DO Austin practiced piano for 8 minutes on Monday. On Tuesday, he practiced piano for 3 times as many minutes. How many minutes did Austin practice piano on Tuesday?

❶ Choose a letter to represent the minutes Austin practiced on Tuesday.

❷ Write an equation. Solve.

❸ Make a model. Use repeated addition to check.

Use __*m*__ to stand for the minutes on Tuesday.

_____ × _____ = __*m*__

_____ = __*m*__

_____ + _____ + _____ = _____

Austin practiced piano for _____ minutes on Tuesday.

B You can use division to solve comparison problems.

DO Elizabeth has 6 red apples. She has 3 times as many red apples as green apples. How many green apples does Elizabeth have?

❶ Choose a letter to represent the number of green apples.

❷ Write an equation. Solve.

❸ Make a model. Use multiplication to check.

Use _____**g**_____ to stand for the green apples.

_____ ÷ _____ = _____**g**_____

_____ = _____**g**_____

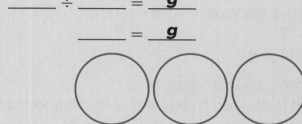

_____ × _____ = _____

Elizabeth has _____ green apples.

How do you check your answer when solving for division?

PRACTICE

Use multiplication or division to solve.

1 There are 4 times as many monkeys as there are apes at a zoo. There are 9 apes. How many monkeys are at the zoo?

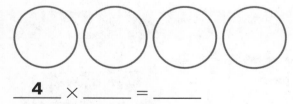

_____**4**_____ × _____ = _____

There are _____ monkeys.

2 Megan made 4 bracelets. Tao made 12 bracelets. How many times more bracelets did Tao make than Megan?

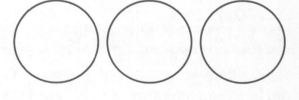

_____ ÷ _____ = _____

Tao made _____ times as many bracelets as Megan.

There will be 45 girls and 40 boys riding in vans to go on a field trip. Each van can hold 9 students. How many vans will be needed to take all the students?

❶ Find the total number of students.

$$45 + 40 = s$$
$$85 = s$$

> Use the letter s to stand for the number of students. Use v to stand for the number of vans needed.

❷ Find the number of vans needed.

$$85 \div 9 = v$$
$$9 \text{ R}4 = v$$

❸ Interpret the **remainder**.
A van is needed to take the 4 remaining students.
So add 1 to the quotient: $9 + 1 = 10$.
10 vans are needed.

Check: 85 rounds to 90, and $90 \div 10 = 9$.
The answer is reasonable.

Words to Know

remainder
a number left over after division has been completed

DISCUSS When solving a division problem with a remainder, how do you decide how to interpret the remainder?

LESSON LINK

PLUG IN	POWER UP	GO!
Using place value can help you add and subtract whole numbers.	You can multiply or divide to solve comparison problems.	

PLUG IN

$$\begin{array}{r} 395 \\ +204 \\ \hline 599 \end{array} \qquad \begin{array}{r} 592 \\ -492 \\ \hline 100 \end{array}$$

POWER UP

Ian read 2 pages. Erika read 4 times as many pages as Ian. How many pages did Erika read?

$$4 \times 2 = 8 \text{ pages}$$

GO!

> I get it! I can use all four operations to solve multi-step word problems.

Use estimation to check your answer.

WORK TOGETHER

Write an equation for each step to solve a multi-step problem.

- Step 1: The equation $9 \times 2 = p$ represents the number of pencils given to the students.

- Step 2: The equation $18 + 45 = b$ represents the number of pencils in the box to begin with.

Mr. Rivera had 63 pencils to begin with.

Mr. Rivera had a box of pencils. He gave 2 pencils to each of 9 students. If 45 pencils are left in the box, how many pencils were in the box to begin with?

Step 1: $9 \times 2 = p$

$$18 = p$$

Step 2: $18 + 45 = b$

$$63 = b$$

A Write an equation for each step to solve.

Chris bought 2 shirts at $11 each and 2 pairs of pants at $13 each. How much did Chris spend in all?

❶ Write equations and solve.

❷ Add to find the total cost.

❸ Check. Round the numbers and compare.

Step 1: Use s to stand for _____.

$2 \times$ _____ $= s$

_____ $= s$

Step 2: Use p to stand for _____.

$2 \times$ _____ $= p$

_____ $= p$

Step 3: _____ $+$ _____ $=$ _____

Check: 22 and 26 are close to 25.

$25 + 25 =$ _____

48 is close to _____. The answer is reasonable.

Chris spent $ _____ in all.

How do you check the answer to a multiplication word problem?

PRACTICE

Write equations to solve. Check your answer.

1 Rachel has 250 beads. She has 79 purple beads, 94 green beads, and the rest are yellow. How many yellow beads does Rachel have?

Step 1: Use b to stand for the number of _____.

_____ + _____ = b

_____ = b

Step 2: Use y to stand for the number of _____.

_____ − _____ = y

_____ = y

Rachel has _____ yellow beads.

Check: Use estimation to decide if your answer is reasonable.

_____

_____

2 Mr. Parker's class has 7 feet of white paper and 8 feet of yellow paper to make posters. They will cut the paper into 2-foot posters. How many posters can they make?

> **HINT**
> You need to interpret the remainder.

Step 1: Use f to stand for _____.

_____ + _____ = f

_____ = f

Step 2: Use p to stand for _____.

_____ ÷ _____ = p

_____ = p

Can the remaining paper be used for a poster? _____

Mr. Parker's class can make _____ posters.

Check: Decide your answer is reasonable.

_____

_____

Solve. Check your answer.

3 Justin has 58 stickers. If he gives 8 stickers to each of his 7 friends, how many stickers will Justin have left?

4 Hanna already has 48 peaches and bought 52 more peaches. She filled each basket with 10 peaches. How many baskets can Hanna fill?

Justin will have _____ stickers left.

Hanna can fill _____ baskets.

Solve.

I'm going to break the problem down into two parts.

5 Katherine bought a calculator for $16 and a book for $27. The total tax for the items is $3. She gave the cashier a $100-bill. How much change will Katherine receive? _____

6 Christian scored nine 2-point baskets and four 3-point baskets while playing basketball. How many points did Christian score in all? _____

Check the Reasoning

Sometimes you need to drop the remainder to find the correct answer.

Julia has 52 inches of ribbon. She thinks that if she cuts it into 9-inch pieces, she will end up with 6 equal pieces of ribbon. Here is her reasoning:

I found 52 ÷ 9 = 5 R7. Since there are 7 inches remaining, I can add 1 more piece to 5. So, I can cut 6 equal pieces of ribbon.

Is Julia correct? Explain why or why not.

PROBLEM SOLVING

BAKE SALE

READ Jonathan is placing 5 cookies in each bag for a bake sale. He has 25 cookies and baked 24 more cookies. How many bags can Jonathan fill?

PLAN • What is the problem asking you to find?

You need to find how many _____ Jonathan can fill.

• What do you need to know to solve the problem?

Jonathan is placing _____ cookies in each bag.

Jonathan has _____ cookies and baked _____ more cookies.

SOLVE Step 1: Use c to stand for _____.

_____ + _____ = c

_____ = c

Step 2: Use b to stand for _____.

_____ ÷ _____ = b

_____ = b

Interpret the remainder.

9 R4 means there are _____ bags with _____ extra cookies.

There are not enough cookies for another bag, so drop the remainder.

CHECK Make a model.

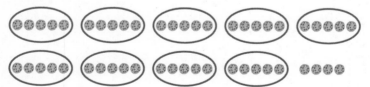

Jonathan can fill _____ bags.

PRACTICE

Use the problem-solving steps to help you.
Check the reasonableness of your answer.

I will use two steps to solve each problem.

1 There are 29 girls and 12 boys. The students will divide into teams of 7. The students who are left over form a smaller team. How many teams are there?

CHECKLIST
- [ ] READ
- [ ] PLAN
- [ ] SOLVE
- [ ] CHECK

2 Dallas has 58 books in his personal library. He has 24 mystery books and 27 science-fiction books. The rest are comic books. How many comic books does Dallas have?

CHECKLIST
- [ ] READ
- [ ] PLAN
- [ ] SOLVE
- [ ] CHECK

3 A store displays its hats on 5 shelves. Each shelf has 3 black hats and 4 gray hats. How many hats does the store have in all?

CHECKLIST
- [ ] READ
- [ ] PLAN
- [ ] SOLVE
- [ ] CHECK

Factors and Multiples

PLUG IN Multiplication and Division Facts

The models represent related **multiplication facts** and **division facts**.

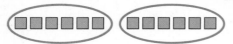

2 groups of 6 equal
12 squares in all.

12 in 2 groups equal
6 in each group.

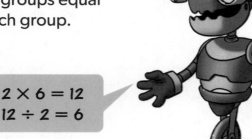

$2 \times 6 = 12$
$12 \div 2 = 6$

6 groups of 2 equal 12 in all.

12 in 6 groups equal 2 in each group.

$6 \times 2 = 12$
$12 \div 6 = 2$

 Words to Know

multiplication fact
a number sentence that joins
equal groups

$$5 \times 2 = 10$$

division fact
a number sentence that separates
equal groups

$$10 \div 5 = 2$$

 DISCUSS What is another way you could separate 10 into equal groups?
What division fact would it show?

A You can write a division fact related to a multiplication fact.

DO Write a division fact related to $3 \times 7 = 21$.

1 Find the total number of objects.

2 Find the number of equal groups.

3 Find the number in each group.

4 Write the division fact.

There are _____ total objects.

There are __**3**__ equal groups.

There are _____ objects in each group.

_____ ÷ _____ = _____.

B You can draw a model to help you write related facts.

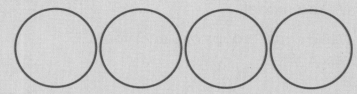

Related facts use the same numbers.

DO Write related multiplication and division facts to show the following:
4 groups of 4 equal 16 in all.
16 in 4 groups equal 4 in each group.

❶ Draw 4 groups. Draw 4 squares in each group.

❷ Write the multiplication fact.

❸ Write the division fact.

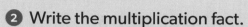

4 groups of 4 equal 16 in all.

_____ × _____ = _____

16 in 4 groups equal 4 in each group.

_____ ÷ _____ = _____

PRACTICE

Write a division fact related to the multiplication fact.

$9 \times 2 = 18$

There are __**18**__ total objects.

There are _____ equal groups.

There are _____ objects in each group.

_____ ÷ _____ = _____

Write 2 related multiplication and division facts that the models show.

__**4**__ groups of _____ equal _____ in all.

_____ × _____ = _____

_____ in __**4**__ groups equal _____ in each group.

_____ ÷ _____ = _____

Unknown Values

This division equation has an **unknown value**.

$18 ÷ \square = 6$

$\square$ is the unknown value.

Make a model.

Make equal groups of 6 until you reach 18.

$\square = 3$

There are 3 groups of 6 counters.

Use a related multiplication fact.

6 times what number equal 18?

$6 × 3 = 18$, so $18 ÷ 3 = 6$.

$\square = 3$

Related facts use the same numbers.

Words to Know

unknown value
a missing number in a number sentence

$$4 × \square = 24$$
$$24 ÷ \square = 4$$

DISCUSS How can you use a multiplication fact to find $36 ÷ 6$?

A You can use a model to find the unknown value.

DO Find the value of $\square$.

$4 × \square = 24$

❶ Count the number of rows and the number of circles in each row.

__4__ equal rows of _____ circles

❷ Write the total.

_____ total circles

❸ Write the unknown value.

$4 × \underline{} = 24$

> **12 is the total and 3 is the number in each group.**

B You can draw a model to find an unknown value.

DO Find the value of □.

$$12 \div \square = 3$$

❶ Draw 12 squares.

❷ Make groups of 3.

❸ Find how many groups.

❹ Write the unknown value.

☐☐☐ ☐ ☐ ☐ ☐ ☐ ☐ ☐ ☐ ☐

There are _____ groups of 3 squares.

$$12 \div \underline{\hspace{1cm}} = 3$$

C You can use a multiplication table to find an unknown value.

DO Find the value of □.

$$28 \div \square = 4$$

❶ Look in the row for 4. Find 28.

❷ Follow the column up from 28 to the number at the top.

❸ Write the factor in the multiplication fact.

❹ Write the unknown value.

×	1	2	3	4	5	6	7
1	1	2	3	4	5	6	7
2	2	4	6	8	10	12	14
3	3	6	9	12	15	18	21
4	4	8	12	16	20	24	28

$$4 \times \underline{\hspace{1cm}} = 28$$

$$28 \div \underline{\hspace{1cm}} = 4$$

DISCUSS How can you use a multiplication table to find the unknown value in □ ÷ 3 = 6?

> **Multiplication Table** can be found on p. 217.

PRACTICE

Find the unknown value.

❶ $4 \times \square = 32$

□ = **8**

❷ $\square \div 5 = 8$

□ = _____

❸ $54 \div \square = 6$

□ = _____

❹ $\square \times 9 = 18$

□ = _____

❺ $36 \div \square = 6$

□ = _____

❻ $35 \div \square = 7$

□ = _____

You can use counters to find **factor pairs** of a number.

●●●●●●●●   ●●●●
            ●●●●

$$1 \times 8 = 8 \qquad 2 \times 4 = 8$$

1×8 and 2×4 are factor pairs of 8.

The factors of 8 are 1, 2, 4, and 8.

8 is a **multiple** of 1, 2, 4, and 8.

I see! A multiple is the product of its factors.

A **composite number** has more than 1 factor pair.

The factor pairs of 9 are 1×9 and 3×3, so 9 is a composite number.

A **prime number** has only 1 factor pair.

The only factor pair of 3 is 1×3, so 3 is a prime number.

5 and 7 are also prime numbers.

The factors of a prime number are 1 and itself.

Words to Know

factor pair Two factors of a number	**multiple** The product of two numbers	**prime number** A number that has only one factor pair, 1 and itself	**composite number** A number that has more than 1 factor pair

DISCUSS Does every number have at least one factor pair? Explain.

LESSON LINK

PLUG IN ➤ **POWER UP** ➤ **GO!**

PLUG IN

Related multiplication and division facts use the same numbers.

● ● ●
● ● ●

$$2 \times 3 = 6$$
$$6 \div 3 = 2$$

POWER UP

Use related facts to find unknown values.

$$5 \times \square = 30$$
$$30 \div \square = 5$$
$$\square = 6$$

GO!

I can use basic facts to find factors and multiples.

WORK TOGETHER

Use Counters to determine if 18 is prime or composite.

$1 \times 18 = 18$

- 18 counters are arranged in 3 different ways.
- There are 3 factor pairs.
- 18 has more than 1 factor pair, so it is a composite number.

$2 \times 9 = 18$ $3 \times 6 = 18$

The factors of 18 are 1, 2, 3, 6, 9, and 18.

18 is a composite number.

Make equal rows and columns.

A Use Counters to find all factors of a number.

DO Determine if 16 is a prime or composite number.

Counters can be found on p. 219.

① Make different arrays for 16 counters.

② Write the factor pairs.

③ List the factors in order.

④ Decide if 16 is prime or composite.

Factor pairs: _____ × _____, _____ × _____,

_____ × _____

Factors of 16: _____, _____, _____, _____, _____

16 is a _____ number.

B Use Counters to find multiples of a number.

DO Find the first four multiples of 4.

① Make 4 groups of 4 counters.

② Write the factor pair for each group.

③ List the multiples of 4.

_____ _____ _____ _____

The first four multiples of 4 are _____, _____,

_____, and _____.

DISCUSS Chelsea says that 21 and 23 are both prime numbers.

Is she correct? Explain why or why not.

Find the factors of each number.

PRACTICE

Find the factor pairs and all of the factors for the number. Use counters to help you.

Counters can be found on p. 221.

HINT
Find different ways to make equal groups from 14.

1 14

Factor pairs: __1__ × _____; __2__ × _____

Factors: __1__, __2__, _____, _____

REMEMBER
List the factors in order.

2 25

Factor pairs: __1__ × __25__; _____ × _____

Factors: _____, _____, _____

3 24

Factor pairs: _____ × _____, _____ × _____, _____ × _____, _____ × _____

Factors: _____, _____, _____, _____, _____, _____, _____, _____

4 32

Factor pairs: _____

Factors: _____

5 39

Factor pairs: _____

Factors: _____

6 42

Factor pairs: _____

Factors: _____

Write *prime* or *composite*.

7 7

_____

8 15

_____

9 27

_____

10 29

_____

Write the next four multiples of each number.

11 9, _____, _____, _____, _____

12 6, _____, _____, _____, _____

Solve.

I can use counters to help find multiples.

13 Carlos says the first four multiples of 7 are 7, 12, 21, and 28. Paul says the first four multiples are 7, 14, 21, and 28. Who is correct?

_____

14 Mia's favorite number is 31. Is her number prime or composite?

_____

 **Missing Multiples**

Anna draws two circles with multiples of 3 and multiples of 4. All of the multiples are less than 30. She used the symbols ● and ■ to represent some missing multiples.

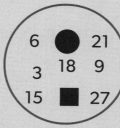

Multiples of 3   Multiples of 4

Write the first 9 multiples of 3 and 4 to compare the two sets.

What are the values of ● and ■?

● = _____

■ = _____

What do you notice about the values of ● and ■?

PROBLEM SOLVING

PACKING SHIRTS

READ

Miguel is packing 48 shirts in boxes to ship.
He can fit 8 shirts in a box.
Will there be 8 shirts in every box?

PLAN

• What is the problem asking you to find?

You need to find whether there will be _____ shirts in every box.

• What do you need to know to solve the problem?

How many shirts is Miguel packing? _____

How many shirts fit in each box? _____

SOLVE

To find the multiples of 8, make groups of 8 counters.

Write number sentences.

$1 \times 8 = 8$ _____ _____ _____ _____ _____

CHECK

Use a multiplication table to see if 48 is a multiple of 8.

×	0	1	2	3	4	5	6	7
6	0	6	12	18	24	30	36	42
7	0	7	14	21	28	35	42	49
8	0	8	16	24	32	40	48	56
9	0	9	18	27	36	45	54	63

Is 48 a multiple of 8? _____

There will be _____ shirts in each box.

PRACTICE

Use the problem-solving steps to help you.

I can use a multiplication table.

1 Mr. Chapman is dividing 35 students into 7 groups. Will he be able to divide the students so that there is the same number in each group? Explain.

CHECKLIST
- [ ] READ
- [ ] PLAN
- [ ] SOLVE
- [ ] CHECK

2 Sonia is planting rows of herbs with 12 herbs in each row. She has 60 herbs to plant. Will each row have the same number of herbs? Explain.

CHECKLIST
- [ ] READ
- [ ] PLAN
- [ ] SOLVE
- [ ] CHECK

3 Melissa is packing 42 glasses into boxes. She can fit 9 glasses in each box. Will there be 9 glasses in each box? Explain.

CHECKLIST
- [ ] READ
- [ ] PLAN
- [ ] SOLVE
- [ ] CHECK

4 Number and Shape Patterns

PLUG IN Even and Odd Numbers

An **even number** of objects can be placed into pairs.

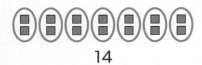

14

All even numbers are **divisible** by 2.

When placing an **odd number** of objects into pairs, there will be 1 left over.

13

All odd numbers are not divisible by 2.

The sum of two equal **addends** will always be an even number.

$4 + 4 = 8$

$9 + 9 = 18$

$11 + 11 = 22$

$20 + 20 = 40$

14 has a 4 in the ones place. So 14 is an even number.

13 has a 3 in the ones place. So 13 is an odd number.

Each equation shows an even sum.

Words to Know

even number a number with 0, 2, 4, 6, or 8 in the ones place	**odd number** a number with 1, 3, 5, 7, or 9 in the ones place	**divisible** able to be divided by a number	**addend** a number to be added

DISCUSS How can you determine if 18 is an even or odd number?

A You can use models to find if a number is even or odd.

DO Is 17 an even or odd number?

❶ Try to make pairs.

❷ See if there is 1 left over.

❸ Write *even* or *odd*.

17 is an _____ number.

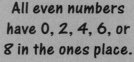

All even numbers have 0, 2, 4, 6, or 8 in the ones place.

B You can look at the ones digit to tell if a number is even or odd.

 Is 20 an odd or even number?

1 Write the number in a place-value chart.

2 Look at the ones digit.

3 Write *even* or *odd*.

Tens	Ones

20 has a _____ in the ones digit.

20 is an _____ number.

C You can write an equation to show an even number.

DO Show 10 as a sum of two equal addends. Write an equation.

1 Show 10 objects in 2 equal rows.

2 Count the number of objects in each row.

3 Write the addends. Find the sum.

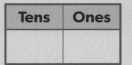

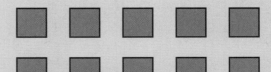

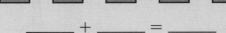

_____ + _____ = _____

PRACTICE

Write *even* or *odd*.

1 11 is an _____**odd**_____ number.

2 24 is an _____ number.

3 36 is an _____ number.

4 45 is an _____ number.

Write an equation to show the even number. Use the number of squares in each row as addends.

5

_____ + _____ = _____

6

_____ + _____ = _____

Identifying Arithmetic Patterns

A **pattern** follows a **rule**.

6, 12, 18, 24, ...

The numbers increase from left to right. Each number is 6 more than the number before it.

$$6 + 6 = 12$$
$$12 + 6 = 18$$
$$18 + 6 = 24$$

A multiplication table shows patterns.

×	1	2	3	4	5	6	
1	1	2	3	4	5	6	$6 \times 1 = 6$
2	2	4	6	8	10	12	$6 \times 2 = 12$
3	3	6	9	12	15	18	$6 \times 3 = 18$
4	4	8	12	16	20	24	$6 \times 4 = 24$

A rule is Add 6.

Look! I see that 6 times a number is always even.

Words to Know

pattern
a group of numbers or figures that follows a rule

rule
tells how to get from one number to the next in a pattern

DISCUSS Explain why the product of a number multiplied by 2 is always even.

A You can find a rule to write the next number in a pattern.

DO Find the rule of the pattern. 46, 51, 56, 61, 66, ...

❶ Decide if the numbers increase or decrease.

❷ Find how many each number is from the number before it.

❸ Write the rule.

The numbers ___increase___ from left to right.

46 + _____ = 51   56 + _____ = 61

51 + _____ = 56   61 + _____ = 66

The rule is _____.

B You can find patterns in the multiplication table.

DO   Describe the pattern shown in the table.

The numbers highlighted are the products.

×	1	2	3	4
1	1	2	3	4
2	2	4	6	8
3	3	6	9	12
4	4	8	12	16

❶ Look at the factors and products in the pattern.

❷ Explain the pattern.

The pattern shows that _____

_____.

DISCUSS   Zoe looks at this pattern: 36, 33, 30, 27, _____. She says the next number is 30. What can you tell Zoe?

PRACTICE

Write the rule.

 ❶ 86, 82, 78, 74, 70, …

The rule is __Subtract__.

❷ 33, 37, 41, 45, 49, …

The rule is _____.

Describe the pattern shown in the table.

❸
×	1	2	3	4
1	1	2	3	4
2	2	4	6	8
3	3	6	9	12
4	4	8	12	16

The pattern shows that

_____

_____.

❹
×	1	2	3	4	5
1	1	2	3	4	5
2	2	4	6	8	10
3	3	6	9	12	15
4	4	8	12	16	20
5	5	10	15	20	25

The pattern shows that

_____

_____.

This **number pattern** has five **terms**.

2, ____, ____, ____, ____
    rule: *Add 8.*

Add 8 to each number to its left.

$$2 + 8 = 10$$
$$10 + 8 = 18$$
$$18 + 8 = 26$$
$$26 + 8 = 34$$

The terms are all even numbers.

2, 10, 18, 26, 34

The rule tells me how to find the other terms in the pattern.

I can also skip count by 8s.

When you add an even number to an even number, the sum is even.

Words to Know

number pattern
a series of numbers that follow a rule
    pattern: 5, 10, 15, 20, …
    rule: *Add 5.*

term
a number in a pattern
    pattern: 2, 4, 6, 8, …
    terms: 2, 4, 6, and 8

DISCUSS Which operations cause whole numbers in a pattern to increase from left to right? Explain.

LESSON LINK

PLUG IN

Whole numbers can be even or odd.

2 is even.   3 is odd.

POWER UP

A rule can be used to identify a pattern.

pattern: 3, 6, 9, 12, 15, 18
rule: *Add 3.*

GO!

I get it! If I know the rule, I can find the numbers in a pattern.

A **shape pattern** uses a rule. Use the rule to find the missing **figure**.

A set of 3 shapes repeat.

Find the missing figure in the pattern.

The ● follows the ▲.

> The set that repeats is the rule.

> The ● is the last figure in the set that repeats.

Words to Know

shape pattern
a series of figures that follow a rule

pattern: ● ▲ ● ▲ ● ▲

rule: ● ▲

figure
a geometric shape

□

DISCUSS How is a shape pattern similar to a number pattern? How is it different?

A You can find a missing figure in a pattern.

DO Find the missing figure in this shape pattern.

● ◯ ● ____ ◯ ● ● ◯ ● ●

❶ Find the set that repeats.   Draw the set that repeats.

❷ Find the missing figure.

Draw the missing figure.

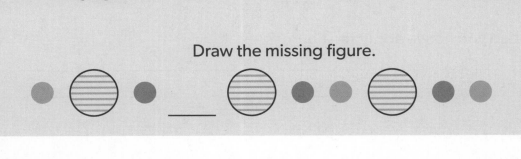

PRACTICE

Complete the pattern. Then answer the question.

1 The rule is *Add 7.*

4, 11, 18, __25__, _____

What do you notice about the terms? _____

_____

2 The rule is *Subtract 5.*

84, 79, 74, _____, _____

What do you notice about the terms? _____

3 The rule is *Multiply by 2.*

2, _____, _____, _____, _____

What do you notice about the terms? _____

4 The rule is *Add 9.*

2, _____, _____, _____, _____

What do you notice about the terms? _____

Find the missing figure in the pattern. Then answer the question.

5   ____

What do you notice about the figures?

_____

_____

6  ___

What do you notice about the figures?

_____

_____

Use the rule to write the other terms in the pattern. Then answer the question.

7 The rule is *Subtract 6.*

48, _____, _____, _____, _____

What do you notice about the terms? _____

_____

8 The rule is  .

What do you notice about the figures?

_____

Solve.

I'm going to look for a pattern.

9 Omar earns money for washing dishes. He earned $2 in the first week, $4 in the second week, $6 in the third week, and $8 in the fourth week. If this pattern continues, how much will Omar earn in the fifth week? _____

10 Elizabeth walks for 25 minutes on Monday, 21 minutes on Tuesday, 17 minutes on Wednesday, and 13 minutes on Thursday. If this pattern continues, how many minutes will Elizabeth walk on Friday? _____

Look for a pattern in the numbers.

 See the Pattern

Chou plays a game with his friends. When he says 7, the answer is 15. When he says 15, the answer is 23. When he says 23, the answer is 31. When Chou says 47, Jessica says the answer is 54. What can you tell Jessica?

What pattern do you see in Chou's game?

PROBLEM SOLVING

READING GAMES

READ

Mrs. Harris uses a pattern to decide how many pages her class should read in a day. The rule is *Divide by 2*. The class reads 32 pages on Monday. Use the rule to find how many pages the class will read on Friday.

PLAN

• What is the problem asking you to find?

How many _____ the class will read on Friday

• What do you need to know to solve the problem?

The class reads _____ pages on Monday.

The rule for the pattern is _____.

SOLVE

Find the terms in the pattern.

32, _____, _____, _____, _____

Use the rule to find the number of pages for each day.

Tuesday: $32 \div 2 =$ _____

Wednesday: _____ $\div 2 =$ _____

Thursday: _____ $\div 2 =$ _____

Friday: _____ $\div 2 =$ _____

CHECK

Use multiplication to check.

$2 \times 2 = 4$

_____ $\times 2 =$ _____

_____ $\times 2 =$ _____

_____ $\times 2 =$ _____

The class will read _____ pages on Friday.

PRACTICE

Use the problem-solving steps to help you.

I will use the rule to make a pattern.

1 Alex uses a pattern to place his car collection into five boxes. He uses the rule *Multiply by 2*. He places 1 car in the first box and 2 cars in the second box. How many cars did Alex place in the rest of the boxes?

CHECKLIST
- [ ] READ
- [ ] PLAN
- [ ] SOLVE
- [ ] CHECK

2 A rule was used to number the apartments where Maya lives. The rule is *Add 4*. The first apartment is numbered 1. What are the next four apartment numbers?

CHECKLIST
- [ ] READ
- [ ] PLAN
- [ ] SOLVE
- [ ] CHECK

3 Ramón uses a rule to decide how long to practice playing piano. The rule is *Add 5 minutes each day*. On Monday, he practices for 10 minutes. How many minutes will he practice on Friday?

CHECKLIST
- [ ] READ
- [ ] PLAN
- [ ] SOLVE
- [ ] CHECK

Reading and Writing Whole Numbers

PLUG IN Whole Numbers

A number can be written in different ways.

Standard form uses **digits**.

4,128

The number is written with digits and a comma.

Expanded form lists the values of the digits.

4,000 + 100 + 20 + 8

The number uses + signs to separate the values.

Number name uses words.

four thousand, one hundred twenty-eight

I can say the number to help write the number in words.

Words to Know	**digits** the numerals 0, 1, 2, 3, 4, 5, 6, 7, 8, and 9	**standard form** a way to write a number using digits	**expanded form** a way to show a number as the sum of the values of the digits	**number name** a way to show a number in words

DISCUSS Give an example of when it would be best to use the expanded form for a number.

A You can use a place-value chart to help you write numbers.

DO Write the number below in expanded form and the number name.

1 Find the value of each digit.

2 List the values with + signs.

3 Say the number aloud.

4 Write the number name.

Thousands	Hundreds	Tens	Ones
3	4	9	8

_____3,000_____ + _____ + _____ + _____

_____

B You can write numbers in different ways.

Write the number below in standard form and the number name.

6,000 + 500 + 40 + 1

For standard form, set a comma between the hundreds and thousands digits.

1 Use a place value chart to help you write the digit of each value.

2 Write the standard form.

3 Use the standard form to say the number out loud. Write the number name.

Thousands	Hundreds	Tens	Ones
6			

standard form

_____

number name

_____

PRACTICE

Write the number in expanded form and the number name.

1

Thousands	Hundreds	Tens	Ones
9	3	1	5

expanded form
___9,000___ + _____ + _____ + _____

number name

_____

_____

2

Thousands	Hundreds	Tens	Ones
2	1	6	0

expanded form
___2,000___ + _____ + _____

number name

_____

_____

Write the number in standard form and the number name.

3 3,000 + 200 + 80 + 7

standard form

_____

number name

_____

_____

4 7,000 + 400 + 30 + 2

standard form

_____

number name

_____

_____

Place Value

The value of a **digit** in a number depends on its position or **place value**.

Thousands			Ones		
Hundreds	**Tens**	**Ones**	**Hundreds**	**Tens**	**Ones**
		2	6	6	3

$$2 \times 1,000 \quad 6 \times 100 \quad 6 \times 10 \quad 3 \times 1$$

$$2,000 \quad\quad 600 \quad\quad 60 \quad\quad 3$$

The value of the hundreds digit is 10 times the value of the tens digit.

Words to Know

place value
the value of a digit based on where it is in a number

digit
the numerals 0, 1, 2, 3, 4, 5, 6, 7, 8, and 9

DISCUSS How is a place-value chart helpful when finding the value of each digit in a number?

A You can use a place-value chart to find the value of each digit.

DO Find the value of each digit in the number below.

1. Write how many thousands.

2. Multiply the digit by its place value.

3. Write the value of the digit.

4. Repeat for the rest of the digits.

Thousands			Ones		
Hundreds	**Tens**	**Ones**	**Hundreds**	**Tens**	**Ones**
		7	3	8	5

___7___ thousands: ___7___ × ___1,000___ = _____

_____ hundreds: _____ × _____ = _____

_____ tens: _____ × _____ = _____

_____ ones: _____ × _____ = _____

B You can use a place-value chart to find the value of a digit.

3 one-thousands = 3 × 1,000

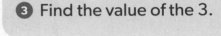 Find the value of the 3 in the number 3,592.

1 Write the number in the chart.

2 Find the digit 3. Write its place-value position.

3 Find the value of the 3.

Thousands			Ones		
Hundreds	Tens	Ones	Hundreds	Tens	Ones
		3			

The 3 is in the _____ place.

The value of the 3 in 3,592 is _____.

 DISCUSS Paige says the value of the 4 in 4,105 is four hundred. What can you tell Paige?

PRACTICE

Find the value of each digit in the number.

1

Thousands			Ones		
Hundreds	Tens	Ones	Hundreds	Tens	Ones
		4	6	5	7

___4___ thousands: ___4___ × _____ = _____

_____ hundreds: _____ × _____ = _____

_____ tens: _____ × _____ = _____

_____ ones: _____ × _____ = _____

Write the value of the underlined digit.

2 1,4̲68 _____

3 1̲,468 _____

4 1,46̲8 _____

5 1,468̲ _____

There are many different ways to write numbers.

Thousands			Ones		
Hundreds	Tens	Ones	Hundreds	Tens	Ones
9	4	8	2	3	5

The standard form uses digits.

948,235

The expanded form lists the values of the digits.

900,000 + 40,000 + 8,000 + 200 + 30 + 5

The number name uses words.

nine hundred forty-eight thousand, two hundred thirty-five

I see! The comma separates the thousands and ones periods.

DISCUSS Give an example of when it would be best to use the number name for a number.

LESSON LINK

| PLUG IN | POWER UP | GO! |

You can write a number in different ways.

standard form

5,831

expanded form

5,000 + 800 + 30 + 1

number name

five thousand, eight hundred thirty-one

Use place value to find the value of each digit in a number.

Hundreds	Tens	Ones
5	6	7

5 hundreds = 500
6 tens = 60
7 ones = 7

I get it! Place value can help me write whole numbers in different ways.

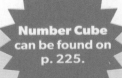
Create a number using the digits rolled from the number cube.

WORK TOGETHER

Use the Number Cube and a place-value chart to write a number in different ways.

- The Number Cube was rolled 6 times.
- The digits are written in the place-value chart.
- The standard form is shown using digits.
- The expanded form is shown listing the value of each digit.

Thousands			Ones		
Hundreds	Tens	Ones	Hundreds	Tens	Ones
4	4	6	2	3	5

standard form

446,235

expanded form

400,000 + 40,000 + 6,000 + 200 + 30 + 5

A Roll the Number Cube to write the digits in the number.

Number Cube can be found on p. 225.

DO Create a number with 6 digits. Write the number in expanded form and the word name.

❶ Roll the cube 6 times. Write the digits in the place-value chart. Start at the hundred thousands place.

Thousands			Ones		
Hundreds	Tens	Ones	Hundreds	Tens	Ones

❷ Write your number in expanded form.

expanded form

_____

❸ Write the number name.

number name

_____

_____

DISCUSS Darpana reads the number 592,103 as five hundred ninety-two thousand, one hundred thirteen. What can you tell Darpana about her number?

Look at the place value of each digit.

PRACTICE

Write the number in expanded form.

1

Thousands			Ones		
Hundreds	Tens	Ones	Hundreds	Tens	Ones
2	9	1	3	5	7

> **REMEMBER**
> Expanded form shows the sum of the values of each digit.

200,000 + _____ + _____ + _____ + _____ + _____

2

Thousands			Ones		
Hundreds	Tens	Ones	Hundreds	Tens	Ones
9	4	6	1	3	8

_____ + _____ + _____ + _____ + _____ + _____

Write the number in expanded form and the number name.

3 724,185

expanded form

_____ + _____ + _____ + _____ + _____ + _____

number name

_____

4 682,413

expanded form

_____ + _____ + _____ + _____ + _____ + _____

number name

_____

Write the number in standard form and expanded form.

5 eight hundred forty-one thousand, three hundred ninety

standard form

_____

expanded form

_____

6 one hundred five thousand, nine hundred thirty-six

standard form

_____

expanded form

_____

Solve.

I need to show the standard form.

7 The library has three hundred sixty-two thousand, one hundred nineteen books. How is that number written using digits? _____

8 Mason wrote a number in expanded form.
400,000 + 20,000 + 300 + 50 + 9
What number did Mason write? _____

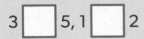**Find the Missing Digits**

There is more than one way to write the same number.

Ariana wrote the same number several different ways. Some of her work was erased. Find the missing digits.

3 ☐ 5, 1 ☐ 2

300,000 + _____ + 5,000 + 100 + _____ + 2

_____ hundred sixty-five thousand, _____ hundred forty two

PROBLEM SOLVING

READING COMPETITION

READ The students of Main Street Elementary read a total of 132,065 pages in one month. What is the number name for the number of pages read?

PLAN
• What is the problem asking you to find?

The _____ for the number of pages read

• What do you need to know to solve the problem?

The number of pages read is _____.

• How can you find the word name?

You can use a place-value chart to help you.

SOLVE Write the digits in the chart.

Thousands			Ones		
Hundreds	Tens	Ones	Hundreds	Tens	Ones

Say the number to write the number name.

_____

CHECK Write the number in expanded form.

_____ + _____ + _____ + _____ + _____

The number name for the number is

_____.

PRACTICE

Use the problem-solving steps to help you.

1 Four thousand, six hundred thirty-one cars drove past a store on Friday. Use the place-value chart to show the number of cars.

Thousands			Ones		
Hundreds	**Tens**	**Ones**	**Hundreds**	**Tens**	**Ones**

CHECKLIST
- [ ] READ
- [ ] PLAN
- [ ] SOLVE
- [ ] CHECK

2 During the month of May, 123,194 people visited the zoo. Show the number of people in expanded form.

CHECKLIST
- [ ] READ
- [ ] PLAN
- [ ] SOLVE
- [ ] CHECK

3 Mr. Smith used the expanded form to show the mileage on his car. He wrote 100,000 + 7,000 + 900 + 80 + 5. What is the mileage on Mr. Smith's car?

CHECKLIST
- [ ] READ
- [ ] PLAN
- [ ] SOLVE
- [ ] CHECK

4 The population of a city is forty-five thousand, seven hundred nine people. What is this number in standard form?

CHECKLIST
- [ ] READ
- [ ] PLAN
- [ ] SOLVE
- [ ] CHECK

Comparing Whole Numbers

Using Models to Compare 3- and 4-Digit Numbers

You can use symbols and words to compare numbers.

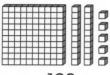 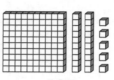

128   125

128 is **greater than** 125.
128 > 125
125 is **less than** 128.
125 < 128

Both numbers have 1 hundred and 2 tens, but 128 has more ones than 125.

Two numbers with the same value are equal.

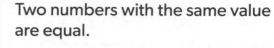

100   100

100 is **equal to** 100.
100 = 100

1 hundred is equal to 10 tens.

Words to Know

greater than (>) a symbol used to show that a number is more than another number

less than (<) a symbol used to show that a number is smaller than another number

equal to (=) a symbol used to show that two numbers have the same value

DISCUSS If you count from 210 to 220, which number do you say first, 218 or 215? How does this help you know which number is greater?

A You can use place-value models to compare numbers.

DO Compare the numbers shown by the models.

① Identify the number each model shows.

② Use words to compare the numbers.

③ Write the correct symbol.

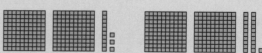

___213___ is less than _____.

____◯____

> The "greater than" symbol opens to the greater number.

B You can use a place-value chart to compare numbers.

DO Compare 2,756 and 2,754.

1. Compare the digits in each place value, starting with the greatest.

2. Find where the digits are different, and compare.

3. Write the correct symbol.

Thousands	Hundreds	Tens	Ones
2	7	5	**6**
2	7	5	**4**

↑   ↑   ↑   ↑

same   same   same **different**

6 ones are _____ than 4 ones.

2,756 ◯ 2,754

PRACTICE

Write the number each model shows. Write >, <, or = to compare.

1

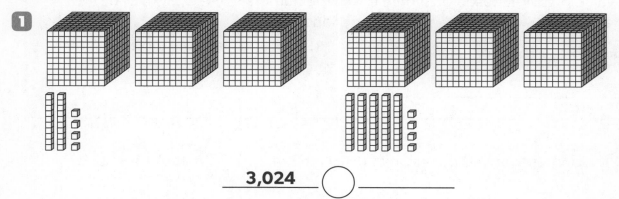

3,024 _____ ◯ _____

Use a place-value chart to compare 6,508 and 6,518. Write >, <, or =.

 2

Thousands	Hundreds	Tens	Ones

↑   ↑   ↑   ↑

same _____ _____ _____

_____ ◯ _____

Place Value

You can use **place value** to find what each **digit** represents in a number.

The place-value chart shows 11,236.

Each digit in 11,236 represents a value.

I see! 1 ten thousand is 10 times greater than 1 thousand.

Ten Thousands	Thousands	Hundreds	Tens	Ones
1	1	2	3	6

↓ ↓ ↓ ↓ ↓

1 ten thousand   1 thousand   2 hundreds   3 tens   6 ones

↓ ↓ ↓ ↓ ↓

10,000   1,000   200   30   6

Words to Know

place value
the value of a digit based on where it is in a number

Thousands	Hundreds	Tens	Ones
4	5	9	1

digit
the numerals 0, 1, 2, 3, 4, 5, 6, 7, 8, and 9

4, 5, 9, and 1 are the digits of 4,591.

DISCUSS   How can you find the value of the digit 2 in 2,163? What is the value?

A You can use place value chart to find the value of a digit in a number.

DO   Find the value of 5 in 25,346.

1 Write the number in the chart.

2 Find the place and the value of the digit 5.

Ten Thousands	Thousands	Hundreds	Tens	Ones
2				

The 5 is in the _____ place.

The value of the 5 is _____, or _____.

B You can use a place-value chart to compare the value of two digits in a number.

I know!
$3,000 = 3 \times 1,000.$

DO Compare the values of the 3s in 63,352.

1 Write the number in the chart.

2 Find the value of each digit 3.

3 Compare the values of the digits.

Ten Thousands	Thousands	Hundreds	Tens	Ones

The 3 in the thousands place has a value of __**3,000**__.

The 3 in the hundreds place has a value of _____.

3 thousands is _____ times greater than 3 hundreds.

DISCUSS Shonda says that the value of 5,000 is 10 more than the value of 500. Is Shonda correct? Explain.

PRACTICE

Write the value of the underlined digit.

1 1,8<u>9</u>2 _____

2 6<u>8</u>,029 _____

3 9<u>4</u>,705 _____

4 2,7<u>5</u>0 _____

Write 24,440 in the place-value chart. Use the chart for problems 6–8.

5

Ten Thousands	Thousands	Hundreds	Tens	Ones

6 The 4 in the _____ place has a value of 4,000.

7 4 thousands is _____ times greater than 4 hundreds.

8 4 _____ is 10 times greater than 4 tens.

Compare 25,418 and 25,428.

Ten Thousands	Thousands	Hundreds	Tens	Ones
2	5	4	**1**	8
2	5	4	**2**	8

The digits in the tens place are different.

25,418 has 1 ten.

25,428 has 2 tens.

1 ten is less than 2 tens, so 25,418 is **less than** 25,428.

25,418 $<$ 25,428

I compared the digits from left to right, starting with the greatest place value—ten thousands.

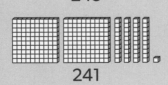

DISCUSS Tyrone said that 37,592 = 37,295 because all of the digits are the same in both numbers. Is he correct? Explain your answer.

LESSON LINK

PLUG IN	POWER UP	GO!

PLUG IN

You can compare numbers using place value and the symbols <, >, or =.

243

241

243 > 241

POWER UP

Each place value is 10 times greater than the place value to its right.

Thousands	Hundreds	Tens	Ones
2	2	5	8

2,000 ↓   200 ↓

2,000 is 10 times greater than 200.

GO!

I get it! Knowing about place value will help me compare numbers!

WORK TOGETHER

Use a place-value chart to compare numbers.

Compare 416,803 and 416,603.

I need to start at the greatest place value and compare one digit at a time.

- The chart shows the numbers 416,803 and 418,603.

- The digits in the thousands place are different.

- 6 thousands is less than 8 thousands.

416,803 is the smaller number.

Hundred Thousands	Ten Thousands	Thousands	Hundreds	Tens	Ones
4	1	6	8	0	3
4	1	8	6	0	3

416,803 is **less than** 418,603.

416,803 < 418,603

A Use a place-value chart to compare numbers.

DO Compare 82,614 and 820,614.

1. Write each number in the place-value chart.

2. Shade the first place value where the digits are different.

Hundred Thousands	Ten Thousands	Thousands	Hundreds	Tens	Ones

3. Use words to compare the numbers.

4. Write a number sentence using the correct symbol.

82,614 is _____ than 820,614.

_____ ◯ _____

DISCUSS Maria is comparing 17,425 and 1,742. Without writing the numbers, explain how you can tell Maria which number is greater.

Count the digits in each number.

PRACTICE

Write the numbers in the place-value chart. Compare using >, <, or =.

1 21,328 and 21,238

Ten Thousands	Thousands	Hundreds	Tens	Ones

__21,328__ ◯ _____

> **HINT**
> The closed end of < or > points to the number with the lesser value.

2 13,335 and 13,336

Ten Thousands	Thousands	Hundreds	Tens	Ones

_____ ◯ _____

3 407,109 and 470,109

Hundred Thousands	Ten Thousands	Thousands	Hundreds	Tens	Ones

_____ ◯ _____

4 380,490 and 38,490

Hundred Thousands	Ten Thousands	Thousands	Hundreds	Tens	Ones

_____ ◯ __38,490__

> **REMEMBER**
> Look for the first place where the digits are different.

Compare using >, <, or =.

5 1,206 ◯ 1,306

6 24,572 ◯ 24,527

7 30,842 ◯ 30,692

8 518,049 ◯ 580,001

9 875,360 ◯ 875,360

10 19,237 ◯ 192,237

Solve.

11 Rae bought a car for $16,060. Maria bought a car for $16,600. Who paid more for a car? _____

> Look! The digits are the same, but they have a different place value in each number.

12 Randy lives in a city with a population of 140,752. Joe lives in a city with a population of 140,725. Who lives in the city with the greater population? _____

> Saying the number out loud can help me compare the values of the numbers.

DISCUSS

Missing Signs

Which symbol makes each statement true? Write >, <, or =.

400 ◯ 4 tens

160 ◯ 16 tens

40 ◯ 400

1,600 ◯ 160

40 ◯ 4 thousands

16 thousands ◯ 16,000

27 thousands ◯ 27 hundreds

630,000 ◯ 63 thousands

270 ◯ 207

6,300 ◯ 630

270,000 ◯ 27 thousands

630 ◯ 63 tens

How can using place value help you compare numbers?

PROBLEM SOLVING

MOUNTAIN HEIGHTS

READ
Mount Whitney in California is 14,494 feet high.
Mount Elbert in Colorado is 14,433 feet high.
Which mountain is taller?

PLAN
• What is the problem asking you to find?

You need to find which mountain is _____.

• What do you need to know to solve the problem?

What is the height of Mount Whitney? _____ feet

What is the height of Mount Elbert? _____ feet

• How can you compare the heights?

You can write the heights in a place-value chart and compare the digits.

SOLVE
Write the height of each mountain in a place-value chart.

Ten Thousands	Thousands	Hundreds	Tens	Ones
1	4	4	9	4
1	4	4	3	3

9 tens is _____ than 3 tens.

14,4**9**4 is _____ than 14,4**3**3.

_____ ◯ _____

CHECK
Use a number line.

14,433   14,494

14,430   14,440   14,450   14,460   14,470   14,480   14,490   15,000

The number 14,494 comes _____ 14,433 on the number line, so it is _____ than 14,433.

Mount _____ is the taller mountain.

PRACTICE

I remember! I need to line up the digits by place value and then compare.

Use the problem-solving steps to help you.

1 Mr. Tang's car has 24,331 miles on it. Mrs. Tang's car has 23,413 miles on it. Whose car has fewer miles?

CHECKLIST
- [ ] READ
- [ ] PLAN
- [ ] SOLVE
- [ ] CHECK

2 Paul earned $3,200 in sales commission in the month of April. He earned $3,275 in commission in May. In which month did Paul earn more commission?

CHECKLIST
- [ ] READ
- [ ] PLAN
- [ ] SOLVE
- [ ] CHECK

3 The McKay family just bought a new home for $150,000. Their previous home cost $148,500. Which home cost more, their new home or their previous home?

CHECKLIST
- [ ] READ
- [ ] PLAN
- [ ] SOLVE
- [ ] CHECK

Adding and Subtracting Whole Numbers

PLUG IN · Properties of Operations

commutative property

$12 + 15 = 15 + 12$

$27 = 27$

> I see! I can add two numbers in any order. The sum will be the same.

associative property

$(10 + 11) + 12 = 10 + (11 + 12)$

$21 + 12 = 10 + 23$

$33 = 33$

> It does not matter how I group the addends. The sum is the same.

Addition and subtraction are **inverse operations**.

```
  13        57
+ 44      - 44
----      ----
  57        13
```

> I see! Inverse operations undo each other.

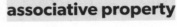

Words to Know

commutative property
the order in which you add two numbers does not change the sum

associative property
the order in which you group three or more addends does not change the sum

inverse operations
operations that undo each other

DISCUSS Give an example of when it would helpful to use the associative property.

A You can use the commutative property to write another equation.

 DO Write another equation for $18 + 12 = 30$.

1 Look at the equation and identify the addends.

The addends are __18__ and _____.

_____ + _____

2 Change the order of the addends. Write the equation.

_____ + _____ = _____

B You can use the associative property to find sums.

 DO   Add (15 + 48) + 22.

1 Group the addends a different way.

2 Add the numbers inside the parantheses. Find the sum.

$$\underline{\quad 15 \quad} + (\underline{\quad\quad} + \underline{\quad\quad}) =$$

$$\underline{\quad\quad} + \underline{\quad\quad} = \underline{\quad\quad}$$

$$(15 + 48) + 22 = \underline{\quad\quad}$$

Look for a 10 in the ones digits of the addends.

C You can use subtraction to check addition problems.

DO   Add 71 + 25.

1 Add to find the sum.

2 Subtract the second addend from the sum to check your answer.

$$\begin{array}{cc} 7 & 1 \\ + 2 & 5 \\ \hline \square & \square \end{array} \qquad \begin{array}{cc} \square & \square \\ - 2 & 5 \\ \hline \square & \square \end{array}$$

PRACTICE

Use the commutative property to write another equation.

1   62 + 18 = 80

$$\underline{\quad 18 \quad} + \underline{\quad\quad} = \underline{\quad\quad}$$

2   75 + 15 = 90

$$\underline{\quad\quad} + \underline{\quad\quad} = \underline{\quad\quad}$$

Use the associative property to find the sum.

3   (21 + 17) + 33

$$\underline{\quad 21 \quad} + (\underline{\quad\quad} + \underline{\quad\quad}) =$$

$$\underline{\quad\quad} + \underline{\quad\quad} = \underline{\quad\quad}$$

4   (25 + 19) + 11

$$\underline{\quad\quad} + (\underline{\quad\quad} + \underline{\quad\quad}) =$$

$$\underline{\quad\quad} + \underline{\quad\quad} = \underline{\quad\quad}$$

Add. Then subtract to check your sum.

5

$$\begin{array}{cc} 4 & 6 \\ + 3 & 3 \\ \hline \square & \square \end{array} \qquad \begin{array}{cc} \square & \square \\ - 3 & 3 \\ \hline \square & \square \end{array}$$

6

$$\begin{array}{cc} 2 & 8 \\ + 5 & 0 \\ \hline \square & \square \end{array} \qquad \begin{array}{cc} \square & \square \\ - 5 & 0 \\ \hline \square & \square \end{array}$$

Adding and Subtracting within 1,000

When adding and subtracting whole numbers, line up the numbers by place value.

Add each place value, starting with the ones places.

$$\begin{array}{r} 1 \\ 191 \\ +327 \\ \hline 518 \end{array}$$

- $1 + 7 = 8$ ones
- $9 + 2 = 11$ tens
  Regroup 11 tens as
  1 hundred and 1 ten.
- $1 + 1 + 3 = 5$ hundreds

Subtract each place value, starting with the ones place.

$$\begin{array}{r} ^{7\,15} \\ 2\cancel{8}\cancel{5} \\ -168 \\ \hline 117 \end{array}$$

- Regroup 8 tens as 7 tens and 10 ones.
  $15 - 8 = 7$ ones
- $7 - 6 = 1$ ten
- $2 - 1 = 1$ hundred

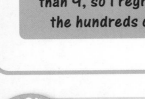

The sum of the digits in the tens place was greater than 9, so I regrouped to the hundreds column.

I could not subtract 8 ones from 5 ones, so I regrouped from the tens column.

DISCUSS Why can you regroup 10 tens as 1 hundred?

A You can use place value to add.

DO Add $482 + 395$.

❶ Line up the addends by place value.

❷ Add the ones. Regroup, if needed.

❸ Add the tens. Regroup, if needed.

❹ Add the hundreds. Write the sum.

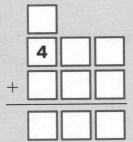

$$482 + 395 = \underline{\hspace{1.5cm}}$$

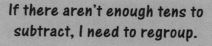

B You can use place value to subtract.

If there aren't enough tens to subtract, I need to regroup.

DO Subtract 849 − 675.

❶ Line up the numbers by place value.

❷ Subtract the ones. Regroup, if needed.

❸ Subtract the tens. Regroup, if needed.

❹ Subtract the hundreds. Write the difference.

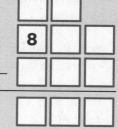

8		
−		

849 − 675 = _____

DISCUSS Caroline says the difference of 495 − 368 = 137. Is Caroline correct? What can you tell Caroline about her work?

PRACTICE

Use place value to add.

❶ 394 + 201 = _____

    3 9 4
 + _____
  ‾‾‾‾‾‾

❷ 518 + 237 = _____

Use place value to subtract.

❸ 586 − 342 = _____

❹ 732 − 408 = _____

❺ 984 − 593 = _____

❻ 612 − 597 = _____

Adding and Subtracting Whole Numbers

Remember that when adding and subtracting whole numbers, you line up the numbers by place value.

Add each place value, starting with the ones place. Regroup if necessary.

$$\begin{array}{r} {\scriptstyle 1 \quad 1} \\ 12{,}402 \\ +\,10{,}758 \\ \hline 23{,}160 \end{array}$$

The sums of the ones and hundreds digits were both greater than 9, so I regrouped.

Subtract each place value, starting with the ones place. Regroup if necessary.

$$\begin{array}{r} {\scriptstyle 8 \quad 11} \\ 39{,}\cancel{1}82 \\ -\,18{,}520 \\ \hline 20{,}662 \end{array}$$

I could not subtract 5 hundreds from 1 hundred, so I regrouped.

 DISCUSS Devin says he can add 39,401 + 10,583 without regrouping. Is Devin correct? Explain.

LESSON LINK

PLUG IN	POWER UP	GO!

PLUG IN

You can use the properties of operations to help you add and subtract.

commutative property
$$36 + 25 = 25 + 36$$
associative property
$$(12 + 25) + 35 = 12 + (25 + 35)$$
inverse operations
$$48 + 31 = 79$$
$$79 - 31 = 48$$

POWER UP

You can use place value to help you add and subtract whole numbers.

$$\begin{array}{r} 218 \\ +\,540 \\ \hline 758 \end{array} \qquad \begin{array}{r} 847 \\ -\,625 \\ \hline 222 \end{array}$$

GO!

I get it! I can use what I know about the properties of operations and place value to add and subtract whole numbers.

WORK TOGETHER

Use Grid Paper to help you line up the digits when you add and subtract.

- The numbers are lined up by place value.

- Start at the ones place, add each column. Regroup to the column to the left when necessary.

- Subtract the sum, 79,813, and one of the addends, 27,679, to check the answer. Regroup when necessary.

The difference, 52,134, matches the other addend. The answer, 79,813, is correct.

> Regroup when a column is 10 or more.

Add 52,134 + 27,679.

			1	1		
	5	2,	1	3	4	
+	2	7,	6	7	9	
	7	9,	8	1	3	

				10		
			7	~~0~~	13	
	7	9,	~~8~~	~~1~~	~~3~~	
−	2	7,	6	7	9	
	5	2,	1	3	4	

A Use Grid Paper to subtract. Use addition to check the difference.

DO Subtract 88,435 − 62,924. Regroup as needed.

❶ Subtract the ones and tens. Regroup when necessary.

❷ Subtract the hundreds and thousands. Regroup when necessary.

❸ Subtract the ten thousands.

❹ Use addition to check.

> **Grid Paper** can be found on p. 229.

88,435 − 62,924 = _____

DISCUSS Brooke finds this sum: 49,104 + 10,583 = 59,687. She says she can use addition to check her answer. Is Brooke correct? Explain.

> I can use an inverse operation to check an answer.

PRACTICE

Complete the addition.

1
```
   1  4, 9  0  2
 + 2  5, 0  8  6
 ▢  ▢  ▢  ▢  ▢
```

2
```
           1
   2  3, 9  7  8
 + 4  4, 0  1  3
 ▢  ▢  ▢  ▢  1
```

REMEMBER
Regroup when the sum of the digits is greater than 9.

Complete the subtraction.

3
```
   3  2, 8  5  2
 − 1  2, 5  1  0
 ▢  ▢  ▢  ▢  ▢
```

4
```
        5  16
   4  3, 6̸  6̸  8
 − 2  1, 5  9  7
 ▢  ▢  ▢  ▢  ▢
```

HINT
Can you subtract 9 tens from 6 tens?

Add or subtract.

5
```
   48,436
 + 20,715
```

6
```
   67,929
 + 28,043
```

7
```
   28,943
 + 51,278
```

8
```
   35,998
 + 18,924
```

9
```
   23,847
 − 10,563
```

10
```
   42,744
 − 11,820
```

11
```
   85,867
 − 56,154
```

12
```
   34,592
 − 13,827
```

Add. Subtract to check the sum.

13
```
   18,115
 +24,317
```

Subtract. Add to check the difference.

14
```
   58,491
 −37,845
```

Solve.

15 13,490 people attended a festival on Saturday. 11,185 people attended on Sunday. How many people attended in all?

_____

I'm going to use addition or subtraction.

16 Last year, the zoo sold 32,481 hats and 45,214 T-shirts. How many more T-shirts than hats did the zoo sell?

_____

Look for key phrases. Add when you want to find how many in all.

 DISCUSS

Check the Reasoning

Rosa wants to find out how many miles in all her family traveled. They flew 2,778 miles. Then they drove 1,035 miles. She wrote her reasoning.

I subtract 1,035 from 2,778 to find the total number of miles traveled.

Is Rosa correct? Explain why or why not.

PROBLEM SOLVING

35,000-MILE WARRANTY

READ Mr. Reed has a 35,000-mile warranty on his car. He has driven his car 28,479 miles. How many more miles can Mr. Reed drive while the car is under warranty?

PLAN • What is the problem asking you to find?

How many more _____ Mr. Reed can drive while the car is under warranty.

• What do you need to know to solve the problem?

How many miles does the warranty cover? _____

How many miles has Mr. Reed driven the car? _____

• How can you solve the problem?

You can use subtraction.

SOLVE Write an equation. Let m = the number of miles Mr. Reed can drive.

____**35,000**____ − ____**28,479**____ = m

Set up the problem vertically. Subtract.

$$
\begin{array}{r}
3\,5,0\,0\,0 \\
-\,2\,8,4\,7\,9 \\
\hline
\end{array}
$$

CHECK Use addition to check.

$$
\begin{array}{r}
6,5\,2\,1 \\
+\,2\,8,4\,7\,9 \\
\hline
\end{array}
$$

Mr. Reed can drive _____ more miles while his car is under warranty.

Be sure to line up the digits by place value.

PRACTICE

Use the problem-solving steps to help you.

1 A charity received $39,019 in donations and gave away $25,318. How much money does the charity have left?

CHECKLIST
- [ ] READ
- [ ] PLAN
- [ ] SOLVE
- [ ] CHECK

2 An office supply store sold 24,738 black pens and 19,392 blue pens. How many pens did it sell in all?

CHECKLIST
- [ ] READ
- [ ] PLAN
- [ ] SOLVE
- [ ] CHECK

3 There are 33,491 students at a college. 24,195 of those students live in the dorms. How many students do not live in the dorms?

CHECKLIST
- [ ] READ
- [ ] PLAN
- [ ] SOLVE
- [ ] CHECK

Multiplying Whole Numbers

PLUG IN Multiplying by Multiples of 10

Multiply 4 × 30.

You can use place-value models to help you find the **product**.

30 is a **multiple of 10**. Show 4 groups of 30.

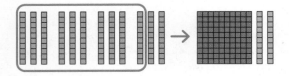

4 × 30 = 120

I can regroup 12 tens as 1 hundred and 2 tens, which equals 120.

You can also use a multiplication fact to find the product.

Think of a fact that has 4 and 3 as factors.

4 × 3 = 12
4 × 30 = 120

I see a pattern!
4 × 3 ones = 12 ones
4 × 3 tens = 12 tens

Words to Know

multiple of 10
10, 20, 30, 40, and so on are multiples of 10.

product
the answer in a multiplication problem

DISCUSS Is 60 a multiple of 10? Explain how you know.

A You can use place-value models to multiply by a multiple of 10.

DO Multiply 6 × 40.

1. Show 6 groups of 40.
2. Regroup 10 tens as 1 hundred. Count the models.
3. Find the product.

24 tens = _____ hundreds and _____ tens

6 × 40 = _____

B You can use multiplication facts to multiply by multiples of 10.

Multiples of 10 have 0 in the ones place.

DO Multiply 8 × 30.

1. Think of a multiplication fact that has 8 and 3 as factors.

2. Use the fact and the pattern to multiply.

3. Write the product.

___**8**___ × ___**3**___ = _____

8 × 3 ones = _____ ones

8 × 3 tens = _____ tens

8 × 30 = _____

C You can find an unknown factor in a number sentence.

DO 2 × □ = 180

1. Think of a multiplication fact that has a factor of 2 and a product of 18.

2. Use the fact and the pattern to find the unknown factor.

3. Write the unknown factor.

___**2**___ × _____ = ___**18**___

2 × _____ ones = 18 ones

2 × _____ tens = 18 tens

2 × _____ = 180

PRACTICE

Write the number sentence that the model shows.

1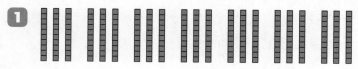

___**7**___ × _____ = _____

Use a multiplication fact to help you find the product.

2 6 × 60 = _____

3 70 × 8 = _____

4 40 × 5 = _____

Find the unknown factor.

5 7 × _____ = 70

6 _____ × 40 = 240

7 3 × _____ = 270

POWER UP — Reading and Writing Whole Numbers

You can use place value to read and write greater numbers.

The chart shows a number with 2 thousands, 5 hundreds, 7 tens, 9 ones.

Thousands	Hundreds	Tens	Ones
2	5	7	9

I see! Expanded form lists the value of each digit.

You can write the number in different ways.

Standard form: 2,579

Word name: two thousand, five hundred seventy-nine

Expanded form: 2,000 + 500 + 70 + 9

DISCUSS How does writing a number in expanded form help you understand place value?

A You can use a place-value chart to write a number name in standard form.

DO Write "five thousand, two hundred sixty-one" in standard form.

① Write the place value for each part of the word name.

② Write the number in the place-value chart.

③ Write the number.

five thousand = ___5___ thousands

two hundred = _____ hundreds

sixty = _____ tens

one = _____ ones

Thousands	Hundreds	Tens	Ones

The number in standard form is _____.

B You can use place value to write a number in expanded form.

If a digit is 0, I do not have to include the value in expanded form.

DO Write 4,065 in expanded form.

❶ Write the number in a place-value chart.

❷ Find the value of each digit.

❸ Write the expanded form.

Thousands	Hundreds	Tens	Ones
4			

4 thousands = _____

0 hundreds = _____

6 tens = _____

5 ones = _____

4,065 in expanded form is _____.

DISCUSS Jay read the number 3,015 as "three thousand, one hundred fifty." Was Jay correct? Explain.

PRACTICE

Place-Value Charts can be found on p. 235.

Write the number name in standard form.

❶ three thousand, eight hundred forty

_____

❷ nine thousand, nineteen

_____

Write the number in expanded form.

❸ 5,672

__5__ thousands = __5,000__

_____ hundreds = _____

_____ tens = _____

_____ ones = _____

5,672 = _____

❹ 7,028

_____ thousands = _____

_____ hundreds = _____

_____ tens = _____

_____ ones = _____

7,028 = _____

You can use a model and the **distributive property** to multiply.

Multiply: 3 × 240.

Write 240 in expanded form.

$$3 \times 240 = 3 \times (200 + 40)$$

Multiply each addend by 3.

$$3 \times (200 + 40) = (3 \times 200) + (3 \times 40)$$

Multiply to find the **partial products**.

$$(3 \times 200) + (3 \times 40) = 600 + 120$$

Add the partial products.

$$600 + 120 = 720$$

I see! I can use the expanded form to split the rectangle.

Words to Know

distributive property
multiplying a sum by a number is the same as multiplying each addend separately and then adding the products

$$2 \times (3 + 4) = (2 \times 3) + (2 \times 4)$$

partial products
the products you add when parts of numbers are multiplied separately

$$(2 \times 3) + (2 \times 4) = 6 + 8 = 14$$

DISCUSS How does a model help you use the distributive property to multiply?

LESSON LINK

PLUG IN

You can use multiplication facts to help you multiply multiples of 10.

$$4 \times 7 = 28$$
$$4 \times 70 = 280$$

POWER UP

You can use place value to write numbers in expanded form.

$$6,132 =$$
$$6,000 + 100 + 30 + 2$$

GO!

I see! I can use multiplication facts and place value to help me use the distributive property to multiply whole numbers.

WORK TOGETHER

You can use an Area Model and the distributive property to multiply whole numbers.

- Write 135 in expanded form.
- Multiply 4 by each addend.
- Multiply to find each partial product.
- Add the partial products.

$4 \times 135 = 540$

Write the greater factor in expanded form.

Multiply 4×135.

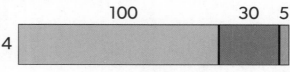

100   30   5

4

$4 \times (100 + 30 + 5)$

$(4 \times 100) + (4 \times 30) + (4 \times 5)$

$400 + 120 + 20$

540

Area Models can be found on p. 239.

A You can use a model and the distributive property to multiply.

DO   Multiply 3×130.

❶ Write 130 in expanded form.

❷ Multiply 3 by each addend.

❸ Find the partial products.

❹ Add the partial products.

130

3

$3 \times 130 = 3 \times (\underline{\quad} + \underline{\quad})$

$(3 \times \underline{\quad}) + (3 \times \underline{\quad})$

$\underline{\quad} + \underline{\quad} = \underline{\quad}$

$3 \times 130 = \underline{\quad}$

B Use the distributive property to multiply.

DO   Multiply 6×352.

❶ Write 352 in expanded form.

❷ Multiply 6 by each addend.

❸ Find the partial products.

❹ Add the partial products.

$6 \times 352 = 6 \times (\underline{\quad} + \underline{\quad} + \underline{\quad})$

$(6 \times \underline{\quad}) + (6 \times \underline{\quad}) + (6 \times \underline{\quad})$

$\underline{\quad} + \underline{\quad} + \underline{\quad} = \underline{\quad}$

$6 \times 352 = \underline{\quad}$

DISCUSS   Explain how you would find the product of 5×32 without using a model.

I can use mental math!

PRACTICE

Use a model and the distributive property to multiply.

1 5 × 130

	100	30
5		

$5 \times 130 = 5 \times (\underline{\hspace{1cm}} + \underline{\hspace{1cm}})$

$\quad\quad\quad\quad = (5 \times \underline{\hspace{1cm}}) + (5 \times \underline{\hspace{1cm}})$

$\quad\quad\quad\quad = \underline{\hspace{1cm}} + \underline{\hspace{1cm}}$

$\quad\quad\quad\quad = \underline{\hspace{1cm}}$

Use the distributive property to multiply.

2 $4 \times 170 = \underline{\hspace{1cm}} \times (\underline{\hspace{1cm}} + \underline{\hspace{1cm}})$

$\quad\quad\quad\quad = (\underline{\hspace{1cm}} \times \underline{\hspace{1cm}}) + (\underline{\hspace{1cm}} \times \underline{\hspace{1cm}})$

$\quad\quad\quad\quad = \underline{\hspace{1cm}} + \underline{\hspace{1cm}}$

$\quad\quad\quad\quad = \underline{\hspace{1cm}}$

Area Models can be found on p. 241.

3 $2 \times 452 = \underline{\quad 2 \quad} \times (\underline{\hspace{1cm}} + \underline{\hspace{1cm}} + \underline{\hspace{1cm}})$

$\quad\quad\quad\quad = (\underline{\hspace{1cm}} \times \underline{\hspace{1cm}}) + (\underline{\hspace{1cm}} \times \underline{\hspace{1cm}}) + (\underline{\hspace{1cm}} \times \underline{\hspace{1cm}})$

$\quad\quad\quad\quad = \underline{\hspace{1cm}} + \underline{\hspace{1cm}} + \underline{\hspace{1cm}}$

$\quad\quad\quad\quad = \underline{\hspace{1cm}}$

REMEMBER Multiply the factor by each addend.

4 $3 \times 301 = \underline{\hspace{1cm}} \times (\underline{\hspace{1cm}} + \underline{\hspace{1cm}})$

$\quad\quad\quad\quad = (\underline{\hspace{1cm}} \times \underline{\hspace{1cm}}) + (\underline{\hspace{1cm}} \times \underline{\hspace{1cm}})$

$\quad\quad\quad\quad = \underline{\hspace{1cm}} + \underline{\hspace{1cm}}$

$\quad\quad\quad\quad = \underline{\hspace{1cm}}$

Draw a model to help you find each product.

5 54 × 3

6 7 × 18

Solve.

I can draw a model.

7 Each student in Mick's class of 24 students collected 5 cans for recycling. How many cans did the students collect in all? _____

8 One hundred fifty students said their favorite sport is basketball. Three times as many students said their favorite sport is football. How many students prefer football? _____

Cross out the digit once it is used.

DISCUSS → **Using Your Number Sense**

A digit is missing from these multiplication equations.

Use one of the digits below to complete each equation. Use each digit only once.

0   1   2   3   4   5   6

2 × 80 = 160   ☐ × 1☐ = 40   3 × ☐1 = 33

☐ × 70 = 420   ☐ × 20 = 100   2☐ × 20 = 460

What strategies did you use to find the missing digits?

PROBLEM SOLVING

TRAIN TRIP

READ An express train has 6 passenger cars. Each passenger car has 28 rows of seats. Each row holds 5 people. How many people can each passenger car hold?

PLAN
- What is the problem asking you to find?

    You need to find the number of _____ each car can hold.

- What do you need to know to solve the problem?

    How many rows are in each passenger car? _____

    How many people can each row hold? _____

- How can you solve the problem?

    You can use the distributive property to multiply.

I didn't need all the information in this problem.

SOLVE Write an equation.
Let p = the number of people each car can hold.

_____ × _____ = p

$5 \times 28 =$ _____ × (_____ + _____)

$\quad = ($ _____ × _____ $) + ($ _____ × _____ $)$

$\quad =$ _____ + _____

$\quad =$ _____

CHECK Use a model to check

$5 \times 20 =$ _____

$5 \times 8 =$ _____

_____ + _____ = _____

	20	8
5		

Each passenger car can hold _____ people.

PRACTICE

I'll need to multiply to solve these problems.

Use the problem-solving steps to help you.

1 Leah divided her garden into 4 sections. She planted 132 seedlings in each section. How many seedlings did she plant in all?

CHECKLIST
- [ ] READ
- [ ] PLAN
- [ ] SOLVE
- [ ] CHECK

2 Jon packed 5 boxes with books. Each box contained 27 books. How many books did he pack in all?

CHECKLIST
- [ ] READ
- [ ] PLAN
- [ ] SOLVE
- [ ] CHECK

3 Mr. Kepler travels a total of 55 miles each day for work. How many miles does he travel in 5 days?

CHECKLIST
- [ ] READ
- [ ] PLAN
- [ ] SOLVE
- [ ] CHECK

Dividing Whole Numbers

PLUG IN   Multiplication and Division Facts

These multiplication and division facts form a **fact family**.

$$3 \times 7 = 21$$
$$7 \times 3 = 21$$
$$21 \div 3 = 7$$
$$21 \div 7 = 3$$

I see! The facts all use the same numbers.

You can use an **unknown factor** to solve a division problem.

Divide $24 \div 6$.

Think: $6 \times \square = 24$

There are 6 groups of 4 circles.

So, $6 \times 4 = 24$ and $24 \div 6 = 4$.

 Words to Know

fact family
a set of related facts that use the same numbers

$$6 \times 8 = 48 \qquad 48 \div 6 = 8$$
$$8 \times 6 = 48 \qquad 48 \div 8 = 6$$

unknown factor
a missing number you multiply by in a multiplication fact

$$\square \times 5 = 35$$

 DISCUSS   How can you find the related multiplication fact for $72 \div 6 = 12$?

A You can use a model to help you find an unknown factor.

DO $7 \times \square = 28$

❶ Draw 7 groups.

❷ Draw a dot in each group until you have drawn 28 dots.

❸ Write how many in each group.

❹ Write the unknown factor.

There are ___7___ groups of _____.

$7 \times$ _____ $= 28$

B You can use a related multiplication fact to solve a division problem.

 DO Divide 18 ÷ 3.

❶ Think: $3 \times \square = 18$

❷ Write the answer to the division problem.

$3 \times \underline{\hspace{1cm}} = 18$

$18 \div 3 = \underline{\hspace{1cm}}$

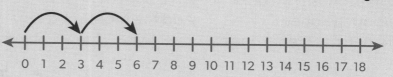
I got it! The unknown factor is the answer to the division problem.

❸ Use a number line to check. Draw jumps of 3 until you reach 18.

0 1 2 3 4 5 6 7 8 9 10 11 12 13 14 15 16 17 18

C You can write a multiplication and division fact family.

 DO Write the fact family for 8, 4, and 32.

❶ Write the multiplication facts.

❷ Write the division facts.

$\underline{\quad 8 \quad} \times \underline{\quad 4 \quad} = \underline{\hspace{1.5cm}}$

$\underline{\hspace{1.5cm}} \times \underline{\hspace{1.5cm}} = \underline{\hspace{1.5cm}}$

$\underline{\hspace{1.5cm}} \div \underline{\hspace{1.5cm}} = \underline{\hspace{1.5cm}}$

$\underline{\hspace{1.5cm}} \div \underline{\hspace{1.5cm}} = \underline{\hspace{1.5cm}}$

PRACTICE

Use a model and a related multiplication fact to solve the division problem.

1 $12 \div 3 = \underline{\hspace{1.5cm}}$

2 $10 \div 2 = \underline{\hspace{1.5cm}}$

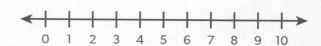
0 1 2 3 4 5 6 7 8 9 10

$3 \times \underline{\quad 4 \quad} = 12$

$2 \times \underline{\hspace{1.5cm}} = 10$

Write the fact family for each set of numbers.

3 8, 7, 56

_____

_____

4 7, 9, 63

_____

_____

Multiplying Whole Numbers

Multiply 2 × 147.

Set up the problem vertically. Line up the digits with the same place value.

Multiply the ones by 2.	Multiply the tens by 2.	Multiply the hundreds by 2.
2 × 7 ones = 14 ones Regroup the ones. 14 ones = 1 ten 4 ones	2 × 4 tens = 8 tens Add the regrouped ten. 8 tens + 1 ten = 9 tens	2 × 1 hundred = 2 hundreds

$$\begin{array}{r} 1 \\ 14\mathbf{7} \\ \times \quad \mathbf{2} \\ \hline 4 \end{array}$$

$$\begin{array}{r} 1 \\ 14\mathbf{7} \\ \times \quad \mathbf{2} \\ \hline 9\,4 \end{array}$$

$$\begin{array}{r} 1 \\ 14\mathbf{7} \\ \times \quad \mathbf{2} \\ \hline 2\,9\,4 \end{array}$$

When the product of a place value is greater than 9, I have to regroup.

147 × 2 = 294

DISCUSS Suppose you are multiplying 143 by 4. Which place value will you multiply first?

A Line up the digits with the same place value to multiply whole numbers.

DO Multiply 3 × 425.

❶ Multiply the ones. Regroup.

❷ Multiply the tens. Add the regrouped ten.

❸ Multiply the hundreds. Regroup.

$$\begin{array}{r} \boxed{1} \\ 4\quad 2\quad 5 \\ \times \qquad\quad 3 \\ \hline \boxed{}\ \boxed{}\ \boxed{}\ \boxed{5} \end{array}$$

3 × 425 = _____

B Set up the problem vertically to find the product.

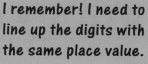

I remember! I need to line up the digits with the same place value.

DO Multiply 2 × 1,947.

1 Multiply the ones. Regroup.

2 Multiply the tens. Add the regrouped ten.

3 Multiply the hundreds. Regroup.

4 Multiply the thousands. Add the regrouped thousand.

```
    □   □
1   9   4   7
×           2
□   □   □   □
```

2 × 1,947 = _____

DISCUSS Jon multiplied 6 × 504 and got a product of 3,004. What did Jon forget to do? What is the correct product?

PRACTICE

Fill in the numbers in the boxes to complete the multiplication.

1 132 × 2 = _____

```
  1   3   2
×         2
□   □   □
```

2 121 × 4 = _____

```
  1   2   1
×         4
□   □   □
```

3 241 × 3 = _____

```
□
  2   4   1
×         3
□   □   □
```

4 482 × 4 = _____

```
□
  4   8   2
×         4
□   □   □   □
```

Find each product. Show your work.

5 628 × 4 = _____

6 1,352 × 6 = _____

Divide 315 ÷ 2.

315 is the **dividend** and 2 is the **divisor**.

Set up the problem vertically.
Divide from left to right.

There are two groups of 1 hundred, 5 tens, and 7 ones. There is 1 one left over.

$$
\begin{array}{r}
157 \text{ R1} \\
2\overline{)315} \\
-2\downarrow \\
\hline
11 \\
-10\downarrow \\
\hline
15 \\
-14 \\
\hline
1
\end{array}
$$

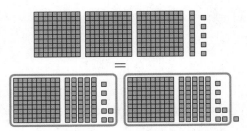

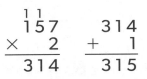

$$
\begin{array}{r}
\overset{1}{1}\ \overset{1}{5}\ 7 \\
\times 2 \\
\hline
314
\end{array}
\qquad
\begin{array}{r}
314 \\
+\ 1 \\
\hline
315
\end{array}
$$

The **quotient** is 157 with a **remainder** of 1.

Use multiplication to check your answer.

Words to Know	**dividend** the number to be divided	**divisor** the number you divide by	**quotient** the answer in a division problem	**remainder** an amount left over when you divide

DISCUSS How can you check the quotient in a division problem when there is a remainder?

LESSON LINK

PLUG IN	**POWER UP**	**GO!**
You can use a multiplication fact related help to solve a division problem. $2 \times 7 = 14 \qquad 7 \times 2 = 14$ $14 \div 7 = 2 \qquad 14 \div 2 = 7$	You can use place value when multiplying greater numbers. $$\begin{array}{r}\overset{2}{7}80 \\ \times 3 \\ \hline 2{,}340\end{array}$$	I see! I can use place value to divide greater numbers. Then I can use multiplication to check my answer.

WORK TOGETHER

You can use Place-Value Models to model division.

Use "R" to indicate the remainder.

Divide 237 ÷ 2.

- Show 2 hundreds, 3 tens, and 7 ones. Show 2 groups.

- Divide the 2 hundreds by 2. There is 1 hundred in each group.

- Divide the 3 tens by 2. There is 1 ten in each group. There is 1 ten left over. Regroup as 10 ones.

- Divide the 17 ones by 2. There are 8 ones in each group. There is 1 one left over.

- Each group has 1 hundred, 1 ten, and 8 ones or 118. There is 1 one left over.

237 ÷ 2 = 118 R1

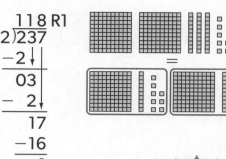

```
     118 R1
  2)237
    -2↓↓
     03↓
    - 2↓
      17
     -16
       1
```

Place-Value Models can be found on p. 243.

A You can use place-value models to help you divide.

DO Divide 458 ÷ 3.

1. Divide the hundreds. Regroup the leftover hundred as tens to make 15 tens.

2. Divide the 15 tens by 3.

3. Divide the 8 ones by 3.

4. Write the quotient.

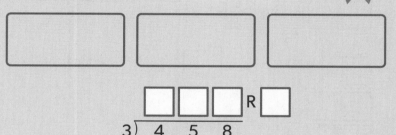

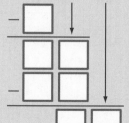

458 ÷ 3 = _____

DISCUSS Explain how you would use place value to locate the first digit in the quotient 860 ÷ 4. What is the quotient?

PRACTICE

Divide. Use place-value models to check your answer.

Place-Value Models can be found on p. 245.

1 105 ÷ 2 = _____

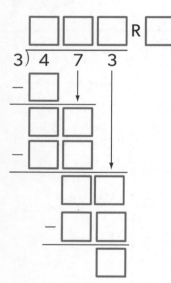

HINT
Make sure you have put an equal number in each group.

2 473 ÷ 3 = _____

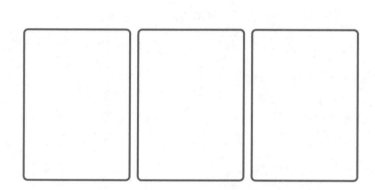

3 250 ÷ 3 = _____

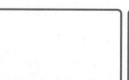 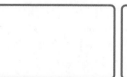 

Divide. Use multiplication to check your answer.

4 645 ÷ 3 = _____

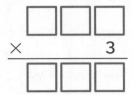

5 284 ÷ 5 = _____

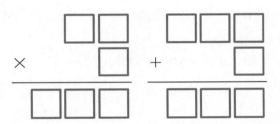

I can solve these problems using division.

Solve.

6 Ali read a 268-page book in 4 days. If she read an equal number of pages each day, how many pages did she read each day? _____

7 A trolley took 453 passengers on 3 tours in one day. If each tour had the same number of passengers, how many passengers went on each tour? _____

Think: As the number of groups increases, what happens to the number in each group?

DISCUSS

Seeing the Trend

Divide.

$2)\overline{210}$ $3)\overline{210}$ $4)\overline{210}$ $5)\overline{210}$ $6)\overline{210}$ $7)\overline{210}$

What do you notice about each quotient as the divisor increases?

PROBLEM SOLVING

MAGAZINES

READ Charlie has 324 magazines to pack in 5 boxes. He will pack the same number of magazines in each box. How many magazines will be in each box? How many magazines are left over?

PLAN
• What is the problem asking you to find?

The number of _____ that will be in each box

• What do you need to know to solve the problem?

He has _____ magazines in _____ equal boxes.

SOLVE Set up the problem and divide.

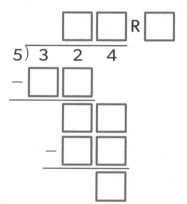

The quotient is _____. So, each box has _____ magazines.

The remainder is _____. So _____ magazines are left over.

CHECK Use multiplication to check.

There will be _____ magazines in each box.

There will be _____ magazines left over.

The remainder is the number left over when the division is complete.

PRACTICE

Use the problem-solving steps to help you.

1 There will be 3 performances of the school play. The school has sold 528 tickets. How many people will attend each performance if an equal number of people attend each performance?

CHECKLIST
- [ ] READ
- [ ] PLAN
- [ ] SOLVE
- [ ] CHECK

2 Brandon poured 250 milliliters of lemonade into 6 small cups. Each cup had the same amount of lemonade. How many milliliters were in each cup? How many milliliters were left over?

CHECKLIST
- [ ] READ
- [ ] PLAN
- [ ] SOLVE
- [ ] CHECK

3 Mr. Willis drove 318 miles over 5 days. He drove the same number of miles on the first four days. On the fifth day he drove 3 more miles than the other days. How many miles did he drive on the first four days? How many miles did he drive on the fifth day?

CHECKLIST
- [ ] READ
- [ ] PLAN
- [ ] SOLVE
- [ ] CHECK

Finding Equivalent Fractions

PLUG IN Understanding Fractions

A **fraction** names part of a whole. The **numerator** tells how many parts of the whole are being described. The **denominator** tells how many equal parts are in the whole.

This circle shows the fraction is $\frac{2}{4}$.

This circle shows the fraction $\frac{2}{3}$.

This whole is split into 4 equal parts, and 2 parts are shaded.

This whole is split into 3 equal parts, and 2 parts are shaded.

Words to Know	fraction a part of a whole	numerator the top number in a fraction that tells how many parts are being described	denominator the bottom number in a fraction that tells the total number of equal parts

 In the fraction $\frac{1}{5}$, what does the 5 represent?

A You can use a model to write a fraction.

 What fraction does the model show?

❶ Write the number of equal parts in the whole.

❷ Write the number of shaded parts.

❸ Write the fraction.

There are ___**5**___ equal parts.

There are _____ shaded parts.

The model shows the fraction $\dfrac{\boxed{}}{\boxed{}}$.

B You can use a model to show a fraction.

 Make a model to show $\frac{7}{10}$.

❶ Start with 1 whole.

❷ Look at the denominator in the fraction. Split the whole into that many equal-sized parts.

❸ Look at the numerator in the fraction. Shade that many parts.

The number of shaded parts is the top number of the fraction.

PRACTICE

Write the fraction shown by the model.

1

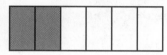

$$\frac{2}{}$$

2

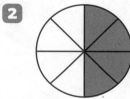

$$\frac{}{}$$

3

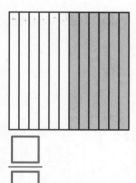

$$\frac{}{}$$

4

$$\frac{}{}$$

Shade the model to show the fraction.

5 $\frac{4}{5}$

6 $\frac{5}{8}$

Understanding Equivalent Fractions

Equivalent fractions have different numerators and denominators, but their values are the same.

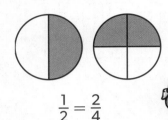

$$\frac{1}{2} = \frac{2}{4}$$

> I see! The circles are divided into different numbers of parts, but the shaded part is the same size.

You can also use **number lines** to show equivalent fractions.

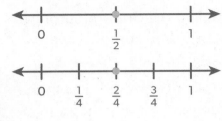

$$\frac{1}{2} = \frac{2}{4}$$

> I get it! Both fractions are the the same point on the number line.

 Words to Know

equivalent fractions
different fractions that name the same amount

number line
a line with tic marks that shows numbers placed in their correct position

 DISCUSS Marla says that $\frac{2}{4}$ and $\frac{2}{5}$ are equivalent fractions. What can you tell Marla?

A You can use fraction models to name equivalent fractions.

DO Name the equivalent fractions.

1. Name the fraction shown by the first model.

2. Name the fraction shown by the second model.

3. Write the equivalent fractions.

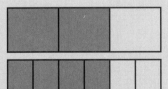

$$\frac{2}{\boxed{}} = \frac{\boxed{}}{\boxed{}}$$

I remember! The denominator tells the number of equal parts between 0 and 1.

B You can use number lines to name equivalent fractions.

 Name the equivalent fractions.

1 Name the fraction shown by the first number line.

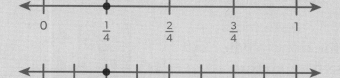

0   $\frac{1}{4}$ $\frac{2}{4}$ $\frac{3}{4}$ 1

2 Name the fraction shown by the second number line.

0   $\frac{1}{8}$ $\frac{2}{8}$ $\frac{3}{8}$ $\frac{4}{8}$ $\frac{5}{8}$ $\frac{6}{8}$ $\frac{7}{8}$ 1

3 Write the equivalent fractions.

$\dfrac{1}{\square} = \dfrac{\square}{\square}$

DISCUSS How can you show the equivalent fractions $\frac{2}{3}$ and $\frac{4}{6}$ using fraction models?

PRACTICE

Name the equivalent fractions shown by the models.

1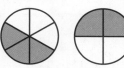

$\dfrac{3}{\square} = \dfrac{\square}{\square}$

2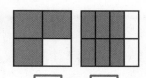

$\dfrac{\square}{\square} = \dfrac{\square}{\square}$

Name the equivalent fractions shown by the number lines.

3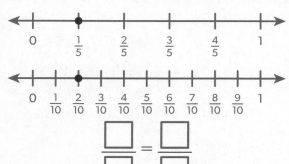

0   $\frac{1}{5}$ $\frac{2}{5}$ $\frac{3}{5}$ $\frac{4}{5}$ 1

0   $\frac{1}{10}$ $\frac{2}{10}$ $\frac{3}{10}$ $\frac{4}{10}$ $\frac{5}{10}$ $\frac{6}{10}$ $\frac{7}{10}$ $\frac{8}{10}$ $\frac{9}{10}$ 1

$\dfrac{\square}{\square} = \dfrac{\square}{\square}$

4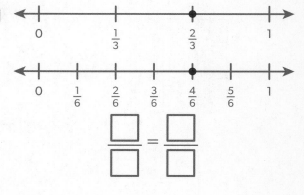

0   $\frac{1}{3}$ $\frac{2}{3}$ 1

0   $\frac{1}{6}$ $\frac{2}{6}$ $\frac{3}{6}$ $\frac{4}{6}$ $\frac{5}{6}$ 1

$\dfrac{\square}{\square} = \dfrac{\square}{\square}$

READY TO GO Finding Equivalent Fractions

You can use multiplication to find equivalent fractions.

Multiply the numerator and the denominator by the same number.

$$\frac{1}{3} = \frac{1}{3} \times \frac{2}{2} = \frac{2}{6}$$

OK! Since $\frac{2}{2}$ is the same as 1, the value of the fractions won't change.

You can use models to check that the fractions are equivalent.

You can use multiplication and models to name more equivalent fractions.

$$\frac{1}{3} = \frac{1}{3} \times \frac{4}{4} = \frac{4}{12}$$

$$\frac{1}{3} = \frac{2}{6} = \frac{4}{12}$$

I see! The size of the shaded region is the same in all of the models.

 How can you find a fraction that is equivalent to $\frac{3}{4}$?

LESSON LINK

PLUG IN

You can use models to name fractions.

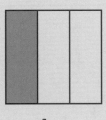

$$\frac{1}{3}$$

POWER UP

You can use models and number lines to find equivalent fractions.

$$\frac{1}{3} = \frac{2}{6}$$

GO!

I get it! I can use models and multiplication to find equivalent fractions.

WORK TOGETHER

Use multiplication and a model to find an equivalent fraction.

- Both the numerator and denominator are multiplied by 2 to get $\frac{2}{20}$.

- The models show $\frac{1}{10}$ and $\frac{2}{20}$.

$\frac{2}{20}$ is an equivalent fraction to $\frac{1}{10}$.

Find an equivalent fraction to $\frac{1}{10}$.

$$\frac{1}{10} = \frac{1}{10} \times \frac{2}{2} = \frac{2}{20}$$

I can multiply the numerator and denominator by the same number.

A You can use multiplication to find an equivalent fraction.

DO Name a fraction that is equivalent to $\frac{2}{5}$.

1. Multiply the numerator and denominator by the same number.

2. Split the fraction model to check your answer.

3. Write the equivalent fraction.

$\frac{2}{5} = \dfrac{2 \times \boxed{}}{5 \times \boxed{}} = \dfrac{\boxed{}}{\boxed{}}$

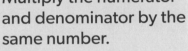

$\frac{2}{5}$ is equivalent to $\dfrac{\boxed{}}{\boxed{}}$.

B You can use multiplication to find an equivalent fraction with a given denominator.

DO Find an equivalent fraction with a denominator of 12 for $\frac{3}{6}$.

1. Think: 6 times what number equals 12?

2. Multiply both the numerator and denominator by that number.

3. Split the fraction model to check your answer.

4. Write the equivalent fraction.

Think: $6 \times \underline{\hspace{1cm}} = 12$

$\frac{3}{6} = \dfrac{3 \times \boxed{}}{6 \times \boxed{}} = \dfrac{\boxed{}}{12}$

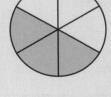

$\frac{3}{6}$ is equivalent to $\dfrac{\boxed{}}{\boxed{}}$.

DISCUSS Taylor said that the fraction $\frac{1}{2}$ is less than $\frac{2}{4}$ since 1 is less than 2. What can you tell Taylor?

I can make a model of the fractions.

PRACTICE

Multiply the numerator and denominator by 2 to find an equivalent fraction.

1

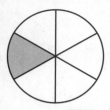

$$\frac{1}{6} = \frac{1 \times \boxed{2}}{6 \times \boxed{}} = \frac{\boxed{}}{\boxed{}}$$

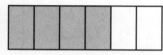

2

$$\frac{4}{6} = \frac{4 \times \boxed{}}{6 \times \boxed{}} = \frac{\boxed{}}{\boxed{}}$$

Multiply the numerator and denominator by 3 to find an equivalent fraction.

3 $\frac{7}{8} = \frac{7 \times \boxed{}}{8 \times \boxed{}} = \frac{\boxed{}}{\boxed{}}$

4 $\frac{4}{5} = \frac{4 \times \boxed{}}{5 \times \boxed{}} = \frac{\boxed{}}{\boxed{}}$

Find an equivalent fraction with a given denominator. Use the model to help you.

5 $\frac{3}{4} = \frac{\boxed{}}{12}$

Think: $4 \times \underline{} = 12$

$$\frac{3}{4} = \frac{3 \times \boxed{}}{4 \times \boxed{}} = \frac{\boxed{}}{12}$$

6 $\frac{2}{5} = \frac{\boxed{}}{20}$

Think: $5 \times \underline{} = 20$

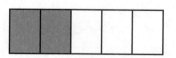

$$\frac{2}{5} = \frac{2 \times \boxed{}}{5 \times \boxed{}} = \frac{\boxed{}}{20}$$

Find an equivalent fraction with a given denominator.

7 $\dfrac{3}{6} = \dfrac{\square}{18}$

Think: $6 \times \underline{\hspace{1cm}} = 18$

$\dfrac{3}{6} = \dfrac{3 \times \square}{6 \times \square} = \dfrac{\square}{\square}$

8 $\dfrac{4}{5} = \dfrac{\square}{50}$

Think: $5 \times \underline{\hspace{1cm}} = 50$

$\dfrac{4}{5} = \dfrac{4 \times \square}{5 \times \square} = \dfrac{\square}{\square}$

Solve.

9 A family ate $\frac{1}{2}$ of a pie for dessert. Write an equivalent fraction for $\frac{1}{2}$.

_____

I can make a model of the fraction.

10 Nancy's garden takes up $\frac{2}{3}$ of her backyard. Write an equivalent fraction for $\frac{2}{3}$.

_____

DISCUSS **Piece of Fabric**

Janae needs $\frac{1}{2}$ yard of fabric for a craft project. Write how much fabric she needs as a fraction with a denominator of 8.

Think: $2 \times \square = 8$.

$$\dfrac{1}{2} = \dfrac{1 \times \square}{2 \times \square} = \dfrac{\square}{8}$$

PROBLEM SOLVING

STICKER TIME

READ

Sarah has a roll of stickers to share with her friends. Everyone will get $\frac{1}{8}$ of the roll. Write an equivalent fraction to $\frac{1}{8}$.

PLAN

• What is the problem asking you to find?

An equivalent fraction to $\dfrac{\Box}{\Box}$

• What do you need to know to solve the problem?

What is the numerator? _____

What is the denominator? _____

• How can you find an equivalent fraction?

I can _____ by 2.

SOLVE

Multiply the numerator and the denominator by 2.

$$\frac{1}{8} = \frac{1 \times \Box}{8 \times \Box} = \frac{\Box}{\Box}$$

CHECK

Use the fraction model to check the answer.

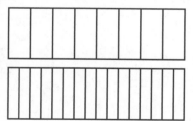

An equivalent fraction to $\frac{1}{8}$ is $\dfrac{\Box}{\Box}$.

PRACTICE

Use the problem-solving steps to help you.

I can multiply the numerator and denominator by the same number.

1 The teacher graded $\frac{1}{5}$ of the tests. What is an equivalent fraction to $\frac{1}{5}$?

CHECKLIST
- [ ] READ
- [ ] PLAN
- [ ] SOLVE
- [ ] CHECK

2 Chloe walked $\frac{2}{6}$ of a mile. What is an equivalent fraction to $\frac{2}{6}$?

CHECKLIST
- [ ] READ
- [ ] PLAN
- [ ] SOLVE
- [ ] CHECK

3 Jason ran $\frac{3}{4}$ of the length of the soccer field to get to the ball. What is an equivalent fraction to $\frac{3}{4}$?

CHECKLIST
- [ ] READ
- [ ] PLAN
- [ ] SOLVE
- [ ] CHECK

Comparing Fractions

Comparing Fractions That Have the Same Numerator or Denominator

When comparing fractions, it is important that the wholes are the same size.

The fractions $\frac{4}{8}$ and $\frac{2}{8}$ have the same **denominator**, but different **numerators**.

The fractions $\frac{2}{8}$ and $\frac{2}{4}$ have the same numerator but different denominators.

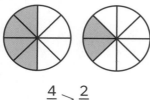

$$\frac{4}{8} > \frac{2}{8}$$

$$\frac{2}{8} < \frac{2}{4}$$

Four eighths are greater than two eighths.

Two eighths are less than two fourths.

Words to Know

denominator
the bottom number in a fraction that tells how many equal parts

numerator
the top number in a fraction that tells how many equal parts are being counted

---

DISCUSS Can you use fractions to compare the size of a slice of an apple to the size of a slice of an orange?

A You can use models to compare fractions with the same denominators.

DO Compare. Write $<$, $>$, or $=$.

$$\frac{3}{6} \bigcirc \frac{5}{6}$$

❶ The denominators are the same.

❷ Compare the numerators to compare the fractions.

❸ Write the correct symbol.

Both wholes are in ___**sixths**___.

3 is _____ than 5.

Three sixths is _____ than five sixths.

$$\frac{3}{6} \bigcirc \frac{5}{6}$$

B You can use models to compare fractions with the same numerators.

 Compare. Write <, >, or =.

$\frac{2}{5} \bigcirc \frac{2}{8}$

❶ The numerators are the same.

❷ Compare the denominators to compare the fractions.

❸ Write the correct symbol.

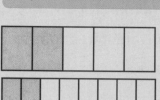

I remember! The denominator tells me the number of equal parts in a whole.

Both wholes have ___**2**___ parts shaded.

Fifths are _____ than eighths.

Two fifths are _____ than two eighths.

$\frac{2}{5} \bigcirc \frac{2}{8}$

PRACTICE

Compare. Write <, >, or =.

1 $\frac{2}{4} \bigcirc \frac{3}{4}$

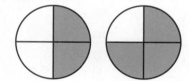

2 $\frac{3}{6} \bigcirc \frac{3}{8}$

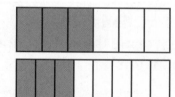

Draw a model for each fraction. Write <, >, or = to compare the fractions.

3 $\frac{5}{8} \bigcirc \frac{7}{8}$

4 $\frac{4}{6} \bigcirc \frac{4}{10}$

Equivalent Fractions

You can use models and multiplication to find **equivalent fractions**.
Multiply the numerator and denominator by the same factor.

Find two equivalent fractions to $\frac{1}{2}$.

Try a factor of 2.

$$\frac{1}{2} = \frac{1}{2} \times \frac{2}{2} = \frac{1 \times 2}{2 \times 2} = \frac{2}{4}$$

The fraction $\frac{2}{2}$ is equal to 1.

Try a factor of 3.

$$\frac{1}{2} = \frac{1}{2} \times \frac{3}{3} = \frac{1 \times 3}{2 \times 3} = \frac{3}{6}$$

The fraction $\frac{3}{3}$ is equal to 1.

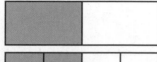

$$\frac{1}{2} = \frac{2}{4}$$

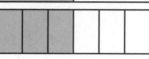

$$\frac{1}{2} = \frac{3}{6}$$

Any number multiplied by 1 has the same value.

I see! $\frac{1}{2}$, $\frac{2}{4}$, and $\frac{3}{6}$ are all equivalent fractions.

Words to Know

equivalent fractions
fractions that name the same amount but have different numerators and denominators

$$\frac{1}{4} = \frac{2}{8} = \frac{3}{12}$$

DISCUSS Why are the numerators and denominators in equivalent fractions not the same?

A You can use fraction models to show equivalent fractions.

DO Draw a fraction model to show $\frac{1}{3} = \frac{2}{6}$.

1 The fraction model shows the fraction $\frac{1}{3}$.

2 Draw an equal-size fraction model.

3 Divide the model into 6 equal parts.

4 Shade 2 parts to show $\frac{2}{6}$.

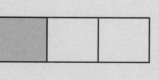

B You can use multiplication to find an equivalent fraction.

A fraction with the same numerator and denominator is equal to 1.

 Write an equivalent fraction for $\frac{2}{5}$.

❶ Choose a factor. Try 2.

❷ Multiply the numerator and denominator by 2.

❸ Write the equivalent fraction.

$$\frac{2}{5} = \frac{2 \times \boxed{2}}{5 \times \boxed{}} = \frac{\boxed{}}{\boxed{}}$$

$$\frac{2}{5} = \frac{\boxed{}}{\boxed{}}$$

DISCUSS How would you find a fraction with a denominator of 9 that is equivalent to $\frac{2}{3}$? What is that equivalent fraction?

PRACTICE

Draw a model to show an equivalent fraction.

1

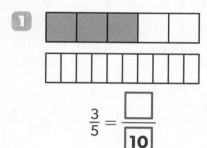

$$\frac{3}{5} = \frac{\boxed{}}{\boxed{10}}$$

2

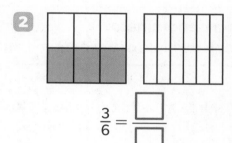

$$\frac{3}{6} = \frac{\boxed{}}{\boxed{}}$$

Find an equivalent fraction by multiplying by 2.

3 $\dfrac{4}{5} = \dfrac{4 \times \boxed{}}{5 \times \boxed{}} = \dfrac{\boxed{}}{\boxed{}}$

4 $\dfrac{3}{4} = \dfrac{3 \times \boxed{}}{4 \times \boxed{}} = \dfrac{\boxed{}}{\boxed{}}$

5 $\dfrac{2}{3} = \dfrac{2 \times \boxed{}}{3 \times \boxed{}} = \dfrac{\boxed{}}{\boxed{}}$

6 $\dfrac{5}{6} = \dfrac{5 \times \boxed{}}{6 \times \boxed{}} = \dfrac{\boxed{}}{\boxed{}}$

You can compare fractions that have different denominators. Change one or both fractions so that they have the same denominator.

Find a common denominator first.

$$\frac{3}{5} \bigcirc \frac{4}{10}$$

Write an equivalent fraction for $\frac{3}{5}$ with a denominator of 10.

Think: $5 \times 2 = 10$

$$\frac{3}{5} = \frac{3 \times 2}{5 \times 2} = \frac{6}{10}$$

$$\frac{3}{5} = \frac{6}{10}$$

Compare the numerators.

$$\frac{6}{10} > \frac{4}{10}$$

$$\frac{3}{5} \bigcirc\!\!> \frac{4}{10}$$

Since 10 is a multiple of 5, use 10 as a common denominator.

I see! Now I can use $\frac{6}{10}$ to compare to $\frac{4}{10}$.

I get it! $\frac{6}{10}$ or $\frac{3}{5}$ is greater than $\frac{4}{10}$, so I use the symbol $>$.

Words to Know

common denominator
a common multiple of the denominators of two or more fractions

DISCUSS Andrea said that $\frac{2}{10}$ is equal to $\frac{2}{5}$. Is she correct? Explain.

LESSON LINK

PLUG IN

You can compare fractions that have different numerators or different denominators.

$$\frac{3}{5} > \frac{3}{8}$$

$$\frac{3}{5} > \frac{2}{5}$$

POWER UP

You can find equivalent fractions by multiplying the numerator and denominator by the same factor.

$$\frac{1}{6} = \frac{1}{6} \times \frac{2}{2}$$

$$= \frac{1 \times 2}{6 \times 2}$$

$$= \frac{2}{12}$$

GO!

I get it! I can compare fractions that have different numerators and denominators by finding equivalent fractions with a common denominator.

WORK TOGETHER

Use Fraction Strips to check your work when comparing fractions.

- A common denominator of 4 and 6 is 12.

- The equivalent fraction for $\frac{2}{4}$ is $\frac{6}{12}$.

- The equivalent fraction for $\frac{4}{6}$ is $\frac{8}{12}$.

- $6 < 8$, so $\frac{6}{12} < \frac{8}{12}$.

- The model shows $\frac{2}{4}$ is less than $\frac{4}{6}$.

Write $<$, $>$, or $=$.

$$\frac{2}{4} \bigcirc \frac{4}{6}$$

Think: 12 is a multiple of both 4 and 6.

Rewrite both fractions with a common denominator of 12.

$$\frac{2}{4} = \frac{2 \times 3}{4 \times 3} = \frac{6}{12} \qquad \frac{4}{6} = \frac{4 \times 2}{6 \times 2} = \frac{8}{12}$$

$$\frac{6}{12} < \frac{8}{12}, \text{ so, } \frac{2}{4} \underbrace{<} \frac{4}{6}.$$

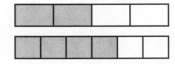

> I can use models to show the two fractions.

> **Fraction Strips** can be found on p.249.

A Find a common denominator to compare fractions.

DO Write $<$, $>$, or $=$.

$$\frac{1}{3} \bigcirc \frac{3}{5}$$

❶ Find a common denominator.

❷ Write equivalent fractions for both fractions with 15 as the denominators.

❸ Compare the numerators to compare the fractions.

❹ Use $<$, $>$, or $=$.

❺ Shade models to check.

15 is a multiple of both _____ and _____.

$$\frac{1}{3} = \frac{1 \times \square}{3 \times \square} = \frac{\square}{\square}$$

$$\frac{3}{5} = \frac{3 \times \square}{5 \times \square} = \frac{\square}{\square}$$

$$\frac{\square}{\square} \bigcirc \frac{\square}{\square}, \text{ so, } \frac{1}{3} \bigcirc \frac{3}{5}.$$

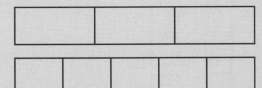

DISCUSS Explain how to find a common denominator for $\frac{3}{6}$ and $\frac{5}{12}$. Name a common denominator.

> I can find the multiples of the denominators.

PRACTICE

Shade the models to compare the fractions. Write <, >, or =.

1 $\frac{3}{5}$ ◯ $\frac{2}{10}$

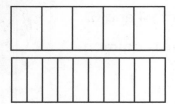

2 $\frac{2}{6}$ ◯ $\frac{4}{8}$

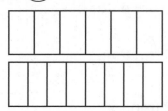

**Find a common denominator. Compare the fractions.
Write <, >, or =.**

Fraction Strips can be found on p. 251.

3 $\frac{2}{6}$ ◯ $\frac{4}{12}$

A common denominator

of 6 and 12 is _____.

$\frac{2}{6} = \frac{2 \times \Box}{6 \times \Box} = \frac{\Box}{\Box}$

4 $\frac{2}{4}$ ◯ $\frac{3}{8}$

A common denominator

of 4 and 8 is _____.

$\frac{2}{4} = \frac{2 \times \Box}{4 \times \Box} = \frac{\Box}{8}$

HINT
8 is a multiple
of 4 and 8.

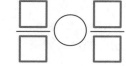

5 $\frac{1}{3}$ ◯ $\frac{2}{5}$

A common denominator

of 3 and 5 is _____.

$\frac{1}{3} = \frac{1 \times \Box}{3 \times \Box} = \frac{\Box}{\Box}$

$\frac{2}{5} = \frac{2 \times \Box}{5 \times \Box} = \frac{\Box}{\Box}$

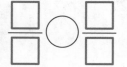

6 $\frac{2}{3}$ ◯ $\frac{1}{2}$

A common denominator

of 3 and 2 is _____.

$\frac{2}{3} = \frac{2 \times \Box}{3 \times \Box} = \frac{\Box}{\Box}$

$\frac{1}{2} = \frac{1 \times \Box}{2 \times \Box} = \frac{\Box}{\Box}$

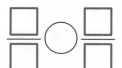

Compare the fractions. Write <, >, or =. Draw models to check.

7 $\frac{1}{4}$ ◯ $\frac{2}{8}$

8 $\frac{3}{4}$ ◯ $\frac{4}{8}$

Solve.

9 Danny read for $\frac{7}{8}$ of an hour. Diego read for $\frac{4}{5}$ of an hour. Who read for longer?

_____

10 Anna jogged $\frac{3}{4}$ of a mile on Monday. She jogged $\frac{5}{6}$ of a mile on Tuesday. On which day did she jog more?

_____

I can draw a fraction model to check my answer.

DISCUSS **Fraction Patterns**

Fill in the missing numbers.

$\frac{1}{2} = \frac{\Box}{4} = \frac{4}{\Box} = \frac{\Box}{16}$

How do you determine the equivalent fraction?

I have to multiply the numerator and denominator by the same number.

PROBLEM SOLVING

SOCCER PLAYERS

READ In the 3rd grade, $\frac{4}{5}$ of the students play soccer. In the 4th grade, $\frac{9}{10}$ of the students play soccer. Which grade has the greater fraction of soccer players?

PLAN
- What is the problem asking you to find?

  The grade that has the greater fraction of _____

- What do you need to know to solve the problem?

  In the 3rd grade, _____ of the students play soccer.

  In the 4th grade, _____ of the students play soccer.

- How can you solve the problem?

  I can compare the fractions.

SOLVE Compare $\frac{4}{5}$ and $\frac{9}{10}$.

_____ is a multiple of 5 and 10. Rewrite $\frac{4}{5}$ with a denominator of 10.

$$\frac{4}{5} = \frac{4 \times \boxed{}}{5 \times \boxed{}} = \frac{\boxed{}}{\boxed{}}$$

Compare the fractions.

$$\frac{\boxed{}}{\boxed{}} \bigcirc \frac{\boxed{}}{\boxed{}}$$

CHECK Make a model for $\frac{4}{5}$ and a model for $\frac{9}{10}$.

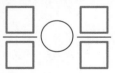

$\frac{4}{5}$ is _____ than $\frac{9}{10}$.

The _____ grade has the greater fraction of soccer players.

PRACTICE

Use the problem-solving steps to help you.

I can make a model of the fractions to help me compare.

1 In Portland, $\frac{2}{5}$ of the population likes vanilla ice cream, and $\frac{5}{10}$ of the population likes chocolate. Which is the preferred flavor?

CHECKLIST
- [ ] READ
- [ ] PLAN
- [ ] SOLVE
- [ ] CHECK

2 Sally has $\frac{3}{6}$ pound of cherries. Cindy has $\frac{4}{8}$ pound of cherries. Who has the greater amount?

CHECKLIST
- [ ] READ
- [ ] PLAN
- [ ] SOLVE
- [ ] CHECK

3 In Maria's class, $\frac{2}{6}$ of the students saw a basketball game over the weekend, and $\frac{7}{12}$ saw a football game. Which sport did more students watch?

CHECKLIST
- [ ] READ
- [ ] PLAN
- [ ] SOLVE
- [ ] CHECK

Adding and Subtracting Fractions and Mixed Numbers

PLUG IN Adding and Subtracting Fractions

You can add or subtract fractions with **like denominators** by adding or subtracting the numerators. The denominator stays the same.

Adding fractions means joining parts.

$$\frac{1}{3} + \frac{1}{3} = \frac{1+1}{3} = \frac{2}{3}$$

| $\frac{1}{3}$ | $\frac{1}{3}$ | |

The **sum** is $\frac{2}{3}$.

I see! There are two $\frac{1}{3}$ pieces.

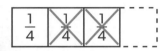

Subtracting fractions means taking away parts.

$$\frac{3}{4} - \frac{2}{4} = \frac{3-2}{4} = \frac{1}{4}$$

| $\frac{1}{4}$ | $\frac{1}{4}$ | $\frac{1}{4}$ | |

The **difference** is $\frac{1}{4}$.

After I take away two $\frac{1}{4}$ pieces, there is one $\frac{1}{4}$ piece left.

Words to Know

| **like denominators** two or more denominators that are the same | **sum** the answer in an addition problem | **difference** the answer in a subtraction problem |

DISCUSS Write an addition or subtraction sentence of 2 fractions with like denominators. Describe the sentence.

A You can use fraction strips to add fractions.

DO Add $\frac{2}{4} + \frac{1}{4}$.

❶ Use two $\frac{1}{4}$ pieces to model $\frac{2}{4}$.

❷ Use one $\frac{1}{4}$ piece to model $\frac{1}{4}$.

❸ Combine and count the number of fraction pieces.

❹ Write the sum.

| $\frac{1}{4}$ | $\frac{1}{4}$ | $\frac{1}{4}$ | |

There are _____ $\frac{1}{4}$ pieces in all.

$$\frac{2}{4} + \frac{1}{4} = \frac{\boxed{}}{\boxed{}}$$

B You can use a fraction strip to subtract fractions.

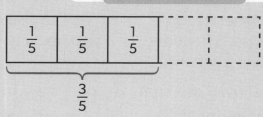

I am taking away parts from $\frac{3}{5}$.

DO Subtract $\frac{3}{5} - \frac{1}{5}$.

❶ Use three $\frac{1}{5}$ pieces to model $\frac{3}{5}$.

❷ Cross out one $\frac{1}{5}$ piece to show $\frac{1}{5}$.

❸ Count the number of fraction pieces left.

❹ Write the difference.

| $\frac{1}{5}$ | $\frac{1}{5}$ | $\frac{1}{5}$ | | |

$\frac{3}{5}$

There are _____ $\frac{1}{5}$ pieces left.

$\frac{3}{5} - \frac{1}{5} = \dfrac{\boxed{}}{\boxed{}}$

C You can add and subtract fractions using paper and pencil.

DO Add $\frac{1}{6} + \frac{4}{6}$.

❶ Check that the fractions have like denominators.

❷ Add the numerators.

❸ Write the sum.

Both fractions have a denominator of _____.

$\frac{1}{6} + \frac{4}{6} = \dfrac{\boxed{} + \boxed{}}{6} = \dfrac{\boxed{}}{\boxed{}}$

PRACTICE

Use fraction strips to add or subtract the fractions.

1

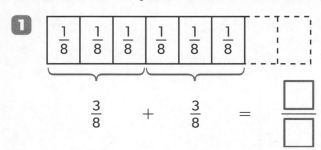

$\frac{3}{8}$ + $\frac{3}{8}$ = $\dfrac{\boxed{}}{\boxed{}}$

2

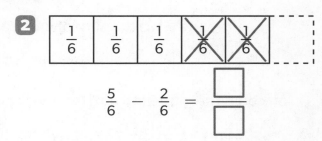

$\frac{5}{6} - \frac{2}{6} = \dfrac{\boxed{}}{\boxed{}}$

Add or subtract.

3 $\frac{7}{10} - \frac{5}{10} = \dfrac{\boxed{}}{\boxed{}}$

4 $\frac{2}{5} + \frac{1}{5} = \dfrac{\boxed{}}{\boxed{}}$

Labeled **Fraction Strips** can be found on p. 257.

POWER UP · Decomposing Fractions

You can separate, or decompose, a fraction into smaller fractions.

You can show $\frac{3}{4}$ as a sum of **unit fractions**.

$$\boxed{\frac{1}{4}} + \boxed{\frac{1}{4}} + \boxed{\frac{1}{4}}$$

$$\frac{3}{4} = \frac{1}{4} + \frac{1}{4} + \frac{1}{4}$$

$\frac{1}{4}$ is a unit fraction because it has 1 in the numerator.

You can also show $\frac{3}{4}$ another way.

$$\boxed{\frac{1}{4}} + \boxed{\frac{1}{4} \;\Big|\; \frac{1}{4}}$$

$$\frac{3}{4} = \frac{1}{4} + \frac{2}{4}$$

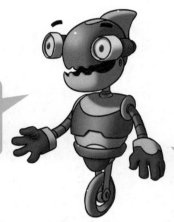

I know! 1 whole is the same as 4 fourths.

You can show a **mixed number** as a sum of smaller fractions.

$$2\frac{1}{4} = 1 + 1 + \frac{1}{4}$$

$\frac{1}{4}$	$\frac{1}{4}$	$\frac{1}{4}$	$\frac{1}{4}$
$\frac{1}{4}$	$\frac{1}{4}$	$\frac{1}{4}$	$\frac{1}{4}$
$\frac{1}{4}$			

$$2\frac{1}{4} = \frac{4}{4} + \frac{4}{4} + \frac{1}{4}$$

Words to Know

unit fraction
a fraction with 1 in the numerator

mixed number
a number that has a whole-number part and a fraction part

DISCUSS To write $\frac{5}{12}$ as the sum of unit fractions, what unit fraction would you use? Explain.

A You can write a fraction as the sum of fractions.

DO Show $\frac{4}{6}$ as the sum of two fractions.

1. Find the correct unit fraction.

2. Find the number of unit fractions that equal $\frac{4}{6}$.

3. Combine the unit fractions to make two fractions.

$$\frac{4}{6} = \frac{\boxed{1}}{6} + \frac{\boxed{}}{6} + \frac{\boxed{}}{6} + \frac{\boxed{}}{6}$$

$$\frac{4}{6} = \frac{\boxed{}}{\boxed{}} + \frac{1}{6}$$

I remember! A fraction with the same numerator and denominator is equal to 1.

B You can write a mixed number as a sum of fractions.

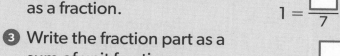 Write $1\frac{2}{7}$ as the sum of fractions.

① Write the mixed number as the sum of the whole-number part and the fraction part.

$$1\frac{2}{7} = \underline{\quad\textbf{1}\quad} + \frac{\square}{\square}$$

② Write the whole-number part as a fraction.

$$1 = \frac{\square}{7} \qquad \frac{2}{7} = \frac{\square}{7} + \frac{\square}{7}$$

③ Write the fraction part as a sum of unit fractions.

④ Write the mixed number as a sum of the fractions.

$$1\frac{2}{7} = \frac{\square}{7} + \frac{\square}{7} + \frac{\square}{7}$$

DISCUSS Could you write $\frac{6}{7}$ as the sum of two fractions in more than one way? Explain.

PRACTICE

Write the fraction as the sum of two fractions.

1 $\frac{5}{9}$

| $\frac{1}{9}$ | $\frac{1}{9}$ | $\frac{1}{9}$ | $\frac{1}{9}$ | $\frac{1}{9}$ | | | | |

$$\frac{5}{9} = \frac{\square}{\square} + \frac{\square}{\square}$$

Write the mixed number as the sum of fractions.

2 $2\frac{2}{3} =$

$$\frac{3}{3} + \frac{\square}{\square} + \frac{\square}{\square} + \frac{\square}{\square}$$

3 $1\frac{2}{4} =$

$$\frac{\square}{\square} + \frac{\square}{\square} + \frac{\square}{\square}$$

Adding and Subtracting Fractions and Mixed Numbers

To add and subtract mixed numbers, rewrite each mixed number as an **improper fraction**. Add $2\frac{1}{3} + 1\frac{1}{3}$.

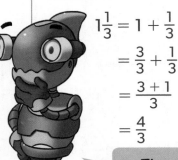

Write $2\frac{1}{3}$ as a sum of fractions.

$$2\frac{1}{3} = 1 + 1 + \frac{1}{3}$$
$$= \frac{3}{3} + \frac{3}{3} + \frac{1}{3}$$
$$= \frac{3 + 3 + 1}{3}$$
$$= \frac{7}{3}$$

The equivalent improper fraction for $2\frac{1}{3}$ is $\frac{7}{3}$.

Write $1\frac{1}{3}$ as a sum of fractions.

$$1\frac{1}{3} = 1 + \frac{1}{3}$$
$$= \frac{3}{3} + \frac{1}{3}$$
$$= \frac{3 + 1}{3}$$
$$= \frac{4}{3}$$

The equivalent improper fraction for $1\frac{1}{3}$ is $\frac{4}{3}$.

Add the improper fractions.

$$\frac{7}{3} + \frac{4}{3} = \frac{11}{3}$$

Rewrite the sum as a mixed number.

$$\frac{11}{3} = \frac{3}{3} + \frac{3}{3} + \frac{3}{3} + \frac{2}{3}$$
$$= 1 + 1 + 1 + \frac{2}{3}$$
$$= 3 + \frac{2}{3}$$
$$= 3\frac{2}{3}$$

Words to Know

improper fraction
a fraction with a numerator that is greater than or equal to the denominator

DISCUSS How would you write $2\frac{1}{2}$ as an improper fraction?

LESSON LINK

PLUG IN	POWER UP	GO!
To add or subtract fractions with like denominators, add or subtract the numerators and keep the denominator. $$\frac{1}{7} + \frac{3}{7} = \frac{4}{7}$$	A mixed number can be written as the sum of fractions with the same denominator. $$2\frac{1}{7} = \frac{7}{7} + \frac{7}{7} + \frac{1}{7}$$	I get it! I can add and subtract mixed numbers by finding equivalent improper fractions. Then, I can add and subtract the improper fractions.

WORK TOGETHER

I can rewrite each whole as 4 fourths.

You can write equivalent improper fractions to add and subtract mixed numbers.

- Write $3\frac{1}{4}$ as $\frac{13}{4}$.
- Write $1\frac{2}{4}$ as $\frac{6}{4}$.
- The difference is $\frac{7}{4}$.
- Write $\frac{7}{4}$ as $1\frac{3}{4}$.

$$3\frac{1}{4} - 1\frac{2}{4} = 1\frac{3}{4}$$

Subtract $3\frac{1}{4} - 1\frac{2}{4}$.

$$3\frac{1}{4} = 1 + 1 + 1 + \frac{1}{4}$$
$$= \frac{4}{4} + \frac{4}{4} + \frac{4}{4} + \frac{1}{4} = \frac{13}{4}$$
$$1\frac{2}{4} = 1 + \frac{2}{4}$$
$$= \frac{4}{4} + \frac{2}{4} = \frac{6}{4}$$
$$3\frac{1}{4} - 1\frac{2}{4} = \frac{13}{4} - \frac{6}{4} = \frac{7}{4}$$
$$\frac{7}{4} = \frac{4}{4} + \frac{3}{4}$$
$$= 1 + \frac{3}{4} = 1\frac{3}{4}$$

A You can write mixed numbers as improper fractions to add.

 Add $1\frac{3}{5} + 2\frac{1}{5}$.

1. Write each mixed number as an improper fraction.
2. Add the improper fractions.
3. Write the answer as a mixed number.

$$1\frac{3}{5} = \frac{\square}{\square} + \frac{\square}{\square} = \frac{\square}{\square}$$

$$2\frac{1}{5} = \frac{\square}{\square} + \frac{\square}{\square} + \frac{\square}{\square} = \frac{\square}{\square}$$

$$1\frac{3}{5} + 2\frac{1}{5} = \frac{\square}{\square} + \frac{\square}{\square} = \frac{\square}{\square}$$

$$\frac{\square}{\square} = \frac{\square}{\square} + \frac{\square}{\square} + \frac{\square}{\square} + \frac{\square}{\square}$$

$$= \underline{\quad} + \underline{\quad} + \underline{\quad} + \underline{\quad}$$

$$1\frac{3}{5} + 2\frac{1}{5} = \underline{\quad}$$

DISCUSS How is adding mixed numbers different than adding fractions?

PRACTICE

Add. Make a model to check your answer.

1 $1\frac{2}{3} + 1\frac{2}{3} =$ _____

$1\frac{2}{3} =$ _____ + _____ = _____ + _____ = _____

$1\frac{2}{3} + 1\frac{2}{3} =$ _____ + _____ = _____

_____ = _____ + _____ + _____ + _____

= _____ + _____ + _____ + _____ = _____

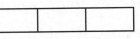
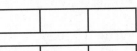

Add or subtract.

2 $2\frac{1}{8} - 1\frac{7}{8} =$ _____

$2\frac{1}{8} =$ _____ + _____ + _____ = _____ + _____ + _____ = _____

$1\frac{7}{8} =$ _____ + _____ = _____ + _____ = _____

$2\frac{1}{8} - 1\frac{7}{8} =$ _____ − _____ = _____

> **HINT**
> Sometimes the answer will not be an improper fraction.

3 $2\frac{4}{6} + 1\frac{1}{6} =$ _____

$2\frac{4}{6} =$ _____ + _____ + _____ = _____ + _____ + _____ = _____

$1\frac{1}{6} =$ _____ + _____ = _____ + _____ = _____

$2\frac{4}{6} + 1\frac{1}{6} =$ _____ + _____ = _____

_____ = _____ + _____ + _____ + _____

= _____ + _____ + _____ + _____ = _____

Add or subtract.

4 $1\frac{2}{7} - \frac{6}{7} = $ _____

5 $\frac{3}{4} + 1\frac{1}{4} = $ _____

Solve.

6 A carpenter will nail a board that is $1\frac{1}{4}$ cm thick to a board that is $2\frac{1}{4}$ cm thick. What is the combined thickness of the boards? _____

> I have to rewrite the mixed numbers as improper fractions.

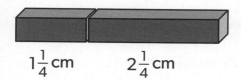

$1\frac{1}{4}$ cm $2\frac{1}{4}$ cm

7 The water in a puddle was $3\frac{1}{5}$ inches deep. After a few hours, the depth decreased by $1\frac{3}{5}$ inches. What is the new depth of the water in the puddle? _____

DISCUSS **Follow the Steps**

Add $\frac{4}{5} + \frac{3}{5} + 2\frac{2}{5}$.

Write the mixed number as an improper fraction:

$2\frac{2}{5} = $ _____ $+$ _____ $+$ _____ $=$ _____ $+$ _____ $+$ _____ $=$ _____

Add the fractions:

$\frac{4}{5} + \frac{3}{5} + $ _____ $= $ _____

Write the answer as a mixed number:

> I separate the improper fraction into as many wholes as I can, with parts of a whole left over.

_____ $=$ _____ $+$ _____ $+$ _____ $+$ _____

$=$ _____ $+$ _____ $+$ _____ $+$ _____

$\frac{4}{5} + \frac{3}{5} + 2\frac{2}{5} = $ _____

PROBLEM SOLVING

RISE AND SHINE!

READ Sultana is making pancakes for breakfast. The recipe calls for $4\frac{1}{4}$ cups of flour. She has already measured $3\frac{2}{4}$ cups. How much more flour does Sultana need to measure?

PLAN • What is the problem asking you to find?

The amount of _____ still needed for the recipe

• What do you need to know to solve the problem?

The recipe calls for _____ cups of flour.

Sultana has measured _____ cups of flour.

• How can you solve the problem?

You need to subtract _____ from _____.

SOLVE Subtract $4\frac{1}{4} - 3\frac{2}{4}$.

Rewrite the mixed numbers as improper fractions.

$4\frac{1}{4} = \dfrac{\boxed{}}{4}$ $3\frac{2}{4} = \dfrac{\boxed{}}{4}$

Subtract the improper fractions: $\dfrac{\boxed{}}{4} - \dfrac{\boxed{}}{4} = \dfrac{\boxed{}}{4}$

CHECK Make a model.

Shade $4\frac{1}{4}$. Then cross out $3\frac{2}{4}$.

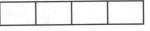

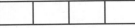

Sultana needs to measure _____ cup more flour.

I can make a model to check my answer!

PRACTICE

Use the problem-solving steps to help you.

1 Luis rode his bike $3\frac{1}{3}$ miles on Saturday and $2\frac{2}{3}$ miles on Sunday. How many miles did he ride in all?

CHECKLIST
- [ ] READ
- [ ] PLAN
- [ ] SOLVE
- [ ] CHECK

2 Agnes has hiked $2\frac{4}{5}$ kilometers of a trail that is $4\frac{1}{5}$ kilometers long. How much farther does she have to go to hike the entire length of the trail?

CHECKLIST
- [ ] READ
- [ ] PLAN
- [ ] SOLVE
- [ ] CHECK

3 Peeta mixes $\frac{7}{8}$ cup of frozen strawberries, $\frac{2}{8}$ cup of frozen blackberries, and $\frac{5}{8}$ cup of frozen blueberries to make a smoothie. How many cups of fruit are in the smoothie? Write your answer as an improper fraction and as a mixed number.

CHECKLIST
- [ ] READ
- [ ] PLAN
- [ ] SOLVE
- [ ] CHECK

Multiplying Fractions by Whole Numbers

PLUG IN Understanding Fractions

The fraction $\frac{2}{4}$ is made up of two $\frac{1}{4}$ parts.

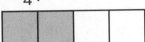

I see! The 2 means two of the parts. The 4 means there are four equal parts in all.

These models show $\frac{1}{4}$.

These models do *not* show $\frac{1}{4}$. The parts are not equal.

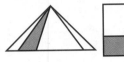

A fraction has a numerator, which is the top number, and a denominator, which is the bottom number.

I get it! The parts must be equal for the model to show a fraction.

DISCUSS Does the model show $\frac{2}{5}$?

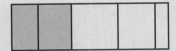

A You can write the fraction that names a model.

DO Write the fraction that names the model.

❶ Find the fraction of the whole each part represents.

❷ Count the shaded parts. Write the numerator.

❸ Count the equal parts. Write the denominator.

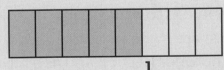

Each part of this whole is ____$\frac{1}{8}$.

[ ] shaded parts
―――――――
[ ] parts in all

The model shows the fraction _____.

B You can identify the model that shows a fraction.

DO Circle the model that shows $\frac{3}{4}$.

1 Count shaded parts and total parts for each model, and write the fraction.

2 Put an X on a model if it does not show a fraction.

3 Circle the model for $\frac{3}{4}$.

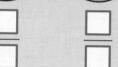

$\dfrac{\boxed{}}{\boxed{4}}$ $\dfrac{\boxed{}}{\boxed{}}$ $\dfrac{\boxed{}}{\boxed{}}$ $\dfrac{\boxed{}}{\boxed{}}$

PRACTICE

Write the fraction shown by the shaded parts of the model.

1 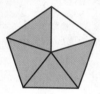 $\dfrac{\boxed{}}{\boxed{5}}$

2 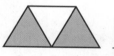 $\dfrac{\boxed{}}{\boxed{}}$

Circle the model that shows $\frac{5}{6}$.

3

Shade the model to show the fraction.

4 $\frac{2}{4}$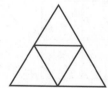

5 $\frac{7}{8}$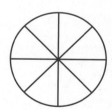

Understanding Fractions as Multiples

You can use models to help you multiply a unit fraction by a whole number.

Multiply $4 \times \frac{1}{3}$.

Show 4 groups of $\frac{1}{3}$.

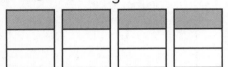

$\frac{1}{3} + \frac{1}{3} + \frac{1}{3} + \frac{1}{3} = \frac{4}{3}$

So, $4 \times \frac{1}{3} = \frac{4}{3}$.

$\frac{4}{3}$ is a **multiple** of $\frac{1}{3}$.

> I get it! I can use repeated addition to find the product.

You can also use a number line to help you multiply.

Multiply $4 \times \frac{1}{3}$.

Make 4 jumps of $\frac{1}{3}$.

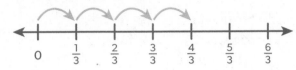

So, $4 \times \frac{1}{3} = \frac{4}{3}$.

> I see! The number line is divided into thirds, and 4 times $\frac{1}{3}$ is $\frac{4}{3}$.

Words to Know

multiple
the product of two numbers

DISCUSS Explain to a classmate how you can find the product of $3 \times \frac{1}{4}$.

A You can use fraction models to multiply a unit fraction by a whole number.

DO Multiply $3 \times \frac{1}{4}$.

❶ Shade 3 models to each show $\frac{1}{4}$.

❷ Write each fraction, and use repeated addition.

❸ Write the product.

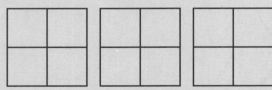

$$3 \times \frac{1}{4} = \frac{\boxed{}}{\boxed{}}$$

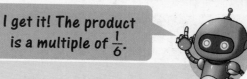

I get it! The product is a multiple of $\frac{1}{6}$.

B You can use a number line to multiply a unit fraction by a whole number.

DO   Multiply $8 \times \frac{1}{6}$.

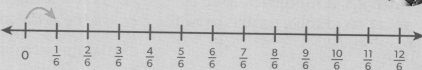

❶ Draw each jump of $\frac{1}{6}$.

❷ Find the number of jumps.

❸ Write the product.

$$8 \times \frac{1}{6} = \frac{\square}{\square}$$

DISCUSS   Explain how you can use a number line to find $6 \times \frac{1}{2}$.

PRACTICE

Shade the model and use repeated addition to multiply.

❶ $5 \times \frac{1}{3} = \dfrac{\square}{\square}$

$$\frac{1}{3} + \underline{} + \underline{} + \underline{} + \underline{} = \underline{}$$

❷ $\frac{1}{2} \times 4 = \dfrac{\square}{\square}$

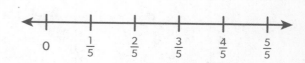

$$\underline{} + \underline{} + \underline{} + \underline{} = \underline{}$$

Use a number line to find the multiple. Draw each jump.

❸ $7 \times \frac{1}{2} = \dfrac{\square}{\square}$

❹ $\frac{1}{5} \times 3 = \dfrac{\square}{\square}$

You can use models or write an equation to solve problems with fractions.

Multiply $4 \times \frac{2}{3}$.

Show 4 groups of $\frac{2}{3}$.

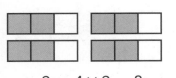

$$4 \times \frac{2}{3} = \frac{4 \times 2}{3} = \frac{8}{3}$$

I see! There are 8 thirds shaded, or $\frac{8}{3}$!

You can also use unit fractions to model and solve the problem.

Separate each $\frac{2}{3}$ into unit fractions.

Think: $\frac{2}{3} = \frac{1}{3} + \frac{1}{3}$

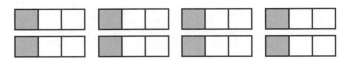

$$8 \times \frac{1}{3} = \frac{8 \times 1}{3} = \frac{8}{3}$$

So, 8 groups of $\frac{1}{3}$ is the same as 4 groups of $\frac{2}{3}$.

Since $8 \times \frac{1}{3} = 4 \times \frac{2}{3}$, then $4 \times \frac{2}{3} = \frac{8}{3}$.

DISCUSS Compare the products of $3 \times \frac{2}{8}$ and $\frac{2}{8} \times 3$.

LESSON LINK

PLUG IN	POWER UP	GO!

PLUG IN

You can use a fraction model to show equal parts of a whole.

$\frac{5}{6}$

POWER UP

You can model and write a fraction as a multiple of a unit fraction.

$$2 \times \frac{1}{4} = \frac{2}{4}$$

$\frac{2}{4}$ is a multiple of $\frac{1}{4}$.

GO!

I can solve word problems with multiplication of a whole number by a fraction.

WORK TOGETHER

You can use Fraction Strips to model a word problem with multiplication of fractions.

- The equation $\frac{2}{5} \times 3 = c$ represents the problem.

- The fraction strips show $\frac{2}{5}$ of 3 wholes. There are 6 shaded fifths.

- Multiply $\frac{2}{5} \times 3 = \frac{6}{5}$.

- Change $\frac{6}{5}$ to a mixed number of $1\frac{1}{5}$.

Mrs. Wiley bought $\frac{6}{5}$ or $1\frac{1}{5}$ pounds of cheese.

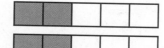

Let *m* represent the amount of mustard.

Mrs. Wiley bought 3 pounds of turkey to make sandwiches for a picnic. She bought $\frac{2}{5}$ as much cheese as turkey. How much cheese did she buy?

$\frac{2}{5} \times 3 = c$

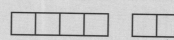

$\frac{2}{5} \times 3 = \frac{2 \times 3}{5} = \frac{6}{5}$

$\frac{6}{5} = \frac{5}{5} + \frac{1}{5} = 1\frac{1}{5}$

Fraction Strips can be found on p. 253.

A You can use Fraction Strips to multiply fractions.

DO Multiply $4 \times \frac{3}{4}$.

1. Shade the fraction strips to show the multiplication.

2. Count the shaded fourths.

3. Multiply the whole number by the numerator. Use the same denominator.

4. Write the product.

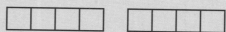

There are _____ shaded fourths.

$4 \times \frac{3}{4} = \dfrac{\boxed{} \times \boxed{}}{4} = \dfrac{\boxed{}}{4}$

$4 \times \frac{3}{4} = \dfrac{\boxed{}}{\boxed{}}$

DISCUSS How can you show and solve $2 \times \frac{4}{5}$?

One of the factors tells me the number of equal groups.

PRACTICE

Shade the fraction models to find the product.

1 Multiply $3 \times \frac{3}{4}$.

HINT
Multiply the whole number by the numerator. Use the same denominator for the product.

$3 \times \frac{3}{4} = \dfrac{\square \times \square}{4} = \dfrac{\square}{4}$

Shade fraction models to help you solve.

2 Charlene collected $\frac{2}{5}$ of a bin of cans to recycle. Juan collected 4 times as many bins as Charlene. How many bins of cans did Juan collect?

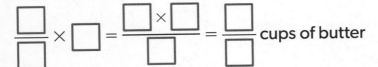

$\square \times \dfrac{\square}{\square} = \dfrac{\square \times \square}{\square} = \dfrac{\square}{\square}$ bins of cans

3 Molly is baking 6 batches of cookies. She needs $\frac{2}{3}$ cup of butter for each batch. How many cups of butter does she need?

$\dfrac{\square}{\square} \times \square = \dfrac{\square \times \square}{\square} = \dfrac{\square}{\square}$ cups of butter

Multiply. Then rewrite the equation as the product of a whole number and a unit fraction.

4 $2 \times \dfrac{3}{4} = \dfrac{\boxed{}}{\boxed{}}$

$\boxed{} \times \dfrac{\boxed{}}{\boxed{}} = \dfrac{\boxed{}}{\boxed{}}$

5 $\dfrac{5}{6} \times 3 = \dfrac{\boxed{}}{\boxed{}}$

$\boxed{} \times \dfrac{\boxed{}}{\boxed{}} = \dfrac{\boxed{}}{\boxed{}}$

Solve.

6 Eric picked 6 pounds of blueberries. He used $\dfrac{3}{4}$ of the blueberries in a muffin recipe. How many pounds of blueberries did he use to make the muffins? _____

I can write an equation, use fraction strips, or use a number line to help me solve.

7 Leo and Sam are collecting newspapers to recycle. Leo collected 2 boxes of newspapers. If Sam collected $\dfrac{5}{8}$ as many boxes as Leo, how many boxes did Sam collect? _____

DISCUSS

Patterns

Marilee sees a pattern in these equations:

$6 \times \dfrac{6}{6} = \dfrac{36}{6}$

$36 \div 6 = 6$

$5 \times \dfrac{5}{5} = \dfrac{25}{5}$

$25 \div 5 = 5$

$4 \times \dfrac{4}{4} = \dfrac{16}{4}$

$16 \div 4 = 4$

$3 \times \dfrac{3}{3} = \dfrac{9}{3}$

$9 \div 3 = 3$

What pattern do you see?

What comes next in the pattern?

A fraction with the same numerator and denominator is equal to 1.

PROBLEM SOLVING

AT THE MARKET

READ

Natalie bought 5 pounds of fruit. Three-fifths of the fruit was apples. How many pounds of apples did she buy?

PLAN

• What is the problem asking you to find?

The number of _____ of apples Natalie bought

• What do you need to know to solve the problem?

How many pounds of fruit did she buy? _____ pounds

What fraction of the fruit she bought was apples? _____

• How can you solve the problem?

You can write an equation and use a number line.

SOLVE

Write an equation to represent the problem.

Let *a* represent the number of pounds of apples.

$\frac{3}{5} \times 5 = a$

Multiply.

$$\frac{3}{5} \times \boxed{5} = \frac{\boxed{} \times \boxed{}}{\boxed{}} = \frac{\boxed{}}{\boxed{}}$$

CHECK

Use a number line. Draw each jump of $\frac{3}{5}$.

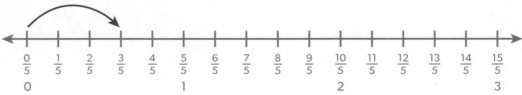

Natalie bought $\frac{\boxed{}}{\boxed{}}$, or _____ pounds of apples.

PRACTICE

Use the problem-solving steps to help you.

I remember! I multiply the whole number by the numerator and keep the denominator.

1 Winn is baking strawberry pies. He has 5 cartons of strawberries. He uses $\frac{3}{8}$ of the strawberries for his first batch of pies. How many cartons of strawberries does he use for the first batch?

CHECKLIST
- [ ] READ
- [ ] PLAN
- [ ] SOLVE
- [ ] CHECK

2 A bakery sold $\frac{2}{3}$ as many plain bagels as sesame bagels. It sold 3 trays of sesame bagels. How many trays of plain bagels did the bakery sell?

CHECKLIST
- [ ] READ
- [ ] PLAN
- [ ] SOLVE
- [ ] CHECK

3 Mrs. Pritchett had 4 cups of sequins for her art students. The students used $\frac{5}{6}$ of the sequins to make their art projects. How many cups of sequins did they use?

CHECKLIST
- [ ] READ
- [ ] PLAN
- [ ] SOLVE
- [ ] CHECK

14 Comparing Decimals

PLUG IN Fractions with Denominators of 10 and 100

You can multiply the numerator and denominator of a fraction by the same number to get an **equivalent fraction**.

Find a fraction with a denominator of 100 that is equivalent to $\frac{1}{10}$.

$$\frac{1}{10} = \frac{1}{10} \times \frac{10}{10} = \frac{1 \times 10}{10 \times 10} = \frac{10}{100}$$

$\frac{1}{10}$ is equivalent to $\frac{10}{100}$.

Multiplying by $\frac{10}{10}$ is the same as multiplying by 1.

The models show the equivalent fractions.

I get it! $\frac{1}{10}$ has the same value as $\frac{10}{100}$.

Words to Know

equivalent fractions
two or more fractions that name the same value but have different numerators and denominators

DISCUSS Explain how you would find a fraction equivalent to $\frac{1}{10}$ with a denominator less than 100. Give an example.

A You can use equivalent fractions to find a missing numerator.

DO Find the missing numerator. $\frac{2}{10} = \frac{\square}{100}$

1 Find the number that you multiply by 10 to get 100.

$10 \times \underline{\textbf{10}} = 100$

2 Multiply the numerator of $\frac{2}{10}$ by that number.

$$\frac{2}{10} = \frac{2}{10} \times \frac{\square}{10} = \frac{2 \times \square}{10 \times 10} = \frac{\square}{100}$$

3 Write the missing numerator.

The missing numerator is _____.

B You can use multiplication to write an equivalent fraction.

 Write a fraction with a denominator of 100 that is equivalent to $\frac{9}{10}$.

❶ Multiply the numerator by 10.

❷ Multiply the denominator by 10.

❸ Write the equivalent fraction.

$$\frac{9}{10} = \frac{9 \times \boxed{10}}{10 \times \boxed{}} = \frac{\boxed{}}{\boxed{}}$$

$\frac{9}{10}$ is equivalent to _____.

I remember! I can multiply the numerator and denominator by the same number.

C You can find if two fractions are equivalent.

 Are $\frac{6}{10}$ and $\frac{62}{100}$ equivalent fractions?

❶ Write a fraction with a denominator of 100 that is equivalent to $\frac{6}{10}$.

❷ Compare the numerator of the new fraction to 62.

$$\frac{6}{10} = \frac{\boxed{} \times \boxed{}}{\boxed{10} \times \boxed{10}} = \frac{\boxed{}}{\boxed{100}}$$

The numerators _____ equivalent.

So, $\frac{6}{10}$ _____ equivalent to $\frac{62}{100}$.

PRACTICE

Find the missing numerator.

❶ $\frac{3}{10} = \frac{\boxed{30}}{100}$

❷ $\frac{8}{10} = \frac{\boxed{}}{100}$

❸ $\frac{4}{10} = \frac{\boxed{}}{100}$

Write an equivalent fraction with a denominator of 100.

❹ $\frac{7}{10} = \frac{\boxed{}}{\boxed{}}$

❺ $\frac{9}{10} = \frac{\boxed{}}{\boxed{}}$

❻ $\frac{5}{10} = \frac{\boxed{}}{\boxed{}}$

Are the fractions equivalent? Write *yes* or *no*.

❼ $\frac{2}{10}, \frac{20}{100}$ _____

❽ $\frac{1}{10}, \frac{11}{100}$ _____

❾ $\frac{6}{10}, \frac{60}{100}$ _____

This grid represents 1 whole. It has 23 out of 100 squares shaded. So, it shows the fraction $\frac{23}{100}$.

The shaded part has 2 full columns, or 2 tenths, plus 3 squares, or 3 hundredths.

You can use a place-value chart to write the **decimal** for $\frac{23}{100}$. The **decimal point** is between the ones place and the tenths place.

Ones	.	Tenths	Hundredths
0	.	2	3

Each square is $\frac{1}{100}$ of the whole grid.

The shaded part shows 23 hundredths, or 2 tenths and 3 hundredths.

I got it! Both $\frac{23}{100}$ and 0.23 can be read as twenty-three hundredths.

Words to Know

decimal	**decimal point**
a number with one or more digits to the right of a decimal point	a period separating the ones from the tenths in a decimal

DISCUSS What decimal is equivalent to the fraction $\frac{40}{100}$? What decimal is equivalent to $\frac{4}{10}$? Are the decimals equivalent? Explain.

A You can use a model to write a fraction as a decimal.

DO Write $\frac{38}{100}$ as a decimal.

1. Count the columns and the squares shaded.
2. Fill in the place-value chart.
3. Write the decimal.

There are ___**3**___ full columns shaded.

There are also _____ squares shaded.

Ones	.	Tenths	Hundredths
0	.		

$\frac{38}{100}$ written as a decimal is _____.

B You can use a place-value chart to write a fraction as a decimal.

 Write $\frac{45}{100}$ as a decimal.

❶ Write the name of the fraction in words.

❷ Write the value of each place.

❸ Fill in the place-value chart.

❹ Write the decimal.

The fraction $\frac{45}{100}$ can be read as

forty-five hundredths.

45 hundredths has __**0**__ ones, _____ tenths, and _____ hundredths.

Ones	.	Tenths	Hundredths
0	.		

$\frac{45}{100}$ written as a decimal is _____.

DISCUSS Gina ate 5 out of 10 strawberries on her plate. How many different ways can you represent 5 out of 10?

PRACTICE

Use the model to write the fraction as a decimal.

❶ $\frac{12}{100} =$ __**0.12**__

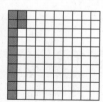

❷ $\frac{6}{100} =$ _____

❸ $\frac{1}{10} =$ _____

Use a place-value chart to write each fraction as a decimal.

❹ $\frac{8}{10} =$ _____

Ones	.	Tenths	Hundredths

❺ $\frac{71}{100} =$ _____

Ones	.	Tenths	Hundredths

READY TO GO Comparing Decimals

You can use a place-value chart and models to compare decimals.

Compare 0.55 and 0.72. Use >, <, or =.

Ones	.	Tenths	Hundredths
0	.	5	5
0	.	7	2

0.55   0.72

Compare the digits, starting with the greatest place value.

Both decimals have 0 in the ones place.

In the tenths place, 5 is less than 7, so 0.55 is less than 0.72.

0.55 < 0.72

> I don't have to compare the hundredths digits. If 0.5 < 0.7, then 0.55 < 0.72.

DISCUSS How would you compare 1.5 and 1.6?

LESSON LINK

PLUG IN	POWER UP	GO!

PLUG IN

You can write a fraction with a denominator of 100 equivalent to a fraction with a denominator of 10.

$$\frac{5}{10} = \frac{5}{10} \times \frac{10}{10}$$
$$= \frac{5 \times 10}{10 \times 10}$$
$$= \frac{50}{100}$$

POWER UP

A fraction with 10 or 100 in the denominator can be written as a decimal.

$\frac{5}{10}$ is *five tenths*.

Five tenths is 0.5.

GO!

> I get it! I can think of fractions with denominators of 10 and 100 to help me compare decimals in tenths and hundredths.

WORK TOGETHER

You can use place value to compare decimals.

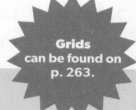
I got it! If I line up the decimal points, then digits with the same place value will line up, too.

- The decimals are lined up on the decimal points.

- Compare the digits, starting with the greatest place value.

- 2.7 is greater than 2.4. Use the symbol >.

Write >, =, or <.

2.7 ◯ 2.4

2.**7**
2.**4**

7 is greater than 4, so 7 tenths is greater than 4 tenths.

2.7 ⟨ > ⟩ 2.4

 A You can use place value and Grids to compare decimals.

Grids can be found on p. 263.

DO Write >, =, or <.

0.60 ◯ 0.62

❶ Line up the decimals on the decimal points.

❷ Compare the digits from left to right

❸ Compare the decimals. Write the symbol.

❹ Shade the models to check.

0.60

_____

Both decimals have _____ in the ones place and _____ in the tenths place.

0 hundredths is _____ than 2 hundredths.

0.60 is _____ than 0.62.

0.60 ◯ 0.62

0.60   0.62

 DISCUSS If you compare two decimals that have the same digits in the same places, what is true? What symbol would you use to compare them?

 I can write an example of the two decimals.

PRACTICE

Shade the models to compare the decimals. Write >, =, or <.

1 0.35 ◯ 0.53

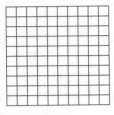 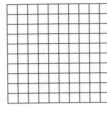

0.35   0.53

35 of 100 squares shaded.

_____ of 100 squares shaded.

Write each decimal in the place-value chart. Write >, =, or < to compare.

2 0.7 ◯ 0.2

Ones	.	Tenths

3 5.1 ◯ 5.5

Ones	.	Tenths

4 2.22 ◯ 2.28

Ones	.	Tenths	Hundredths

5 0.67 ◯ 0.72

Ones	.	Tenths	Hundredths

6 1.8 ◯ 1.73

Ones	.	Tenths	Hundredths

7 0.9 ◯ 0.99

Ones	.	Tenths	Hundredths

Compare the decimals. Write >, =, or <.

8 3.8 ◯ 3.5

9 0.6 ◯ 0.6

10 7.24 ◯ 7.25

11 2.70 ◯ 1.75

Solve.

Comparing amounts of money is the same as comparing decimals.

12 Sandra's bottle holds 1.4 liters of water, and Johnny's bottle holds 1.2 liters. Whose bottle holds more water? _____

13 Huan has $1.78 in her piggy bank. Jim has $2.24 in his coin jar. Who has more money? _____

DISCUSS

Think Through the Process

Jeremiah wants to compare 5.75 and 6.65.

These numbers have different digits in the ones place.

First, he compares the digits in the hundredths place. They are the same. Then, he compares the digits in the tenths place. Since 7 > 5, he decides that 5.75 > 6.65.

Is Jeremiah correct? Explain.

PROBLEM SOLVING

LEMONS INTO LEMONADE

READ

Ravi has a pitcher that holds 0.8 gallon. He plans to make 0.7 gallon of lemonade for a party. Will his pitcher hold all of the lemonade?

PLAN

• What is the problem asking you to find?

Decide if Ravi's pitcher will hold _____ gallons of lemonade.

• What do you need to do to solve the problem?

You need to compare the decimals _____ and _____.

• How will you find the answer?

If 0.8 gallon is greater than 0.7 gallon, then the pitcher _____ hold all of the lemonade.

SOLVE

Write the decimals in the place-value chart.

Ones	.	Tenths

Compare the digits in the _____ place.

Then compare the digits in the _____ place.

Write >, =, or < to compare the decimals.

0.8 ◯ 0.7

CHECK

Find both decimals on the number line.

The decimal that is farther to the right is the greater number.

0   0.1   0.2   0.3   0.4   0.5   0.6   0.7   0.8   0.9   1

The decimal _____ is farther to the right on the number line.

The pitcher _____ hold all of the lemonade for Ravi's party.

PRACTICE

Use the problem-solving steps to help you.

1 A lollipop costs $0.89, and Sasha has $0.65. Does Sasha have enough money to buy the lollipop?

2 A scientist needs at least 1.35 grams of baking soda to do an experiment. She has 1.38 grams. Can the scientist do the experiment?

3 Three athletes competed in a short race. Their times are shown in the table. Who had the fastest time?

Name	Time
Kaylee	3.4 minutes
Elaina	2.1 minutes
William	2.9 minutes

A faster time means a shorter time.

Solving Measurement Problems

PLUG IN Operations with Fractions

Fraction models can help you add and subtract fractions.

$$\frac{3}{8} + \frac{4}{8} = \square$$

Add the numerators, and then write the denominator.

$$\frac{3}{8} + \frac{4}{8} = \frac{7}{8}$$

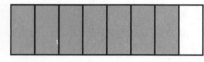

You can subtract to check your answer.

$$\frac{7}{8} - \frac{4}{8} = \frac{3}{8}$$

You can use fraction models to help you multiply fractions.

$$3 \times \frac{1}{4} = \square$$

Multiply the numerator of the fraction by the whole number, and then use the denominator of the fraction as the denominator of the product.

$$3 \times \frac{1}{4} = \frac{3 \times 1}{4} = \frac{3}{4}$$

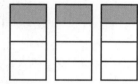

The model shows that 3 groups of $\frac{1}{4}$ is $\frac{3}{4}$.

DISCUSS Explain how you could use addition to check your answer when multiplying $3 \times \frac{1}{4}$.

A You can use models to help you add fractions.

 Add $\frac{4}{10} + \frac{5}{10}$.

❶ Add the numerators. Write the denominator.

❷ Write the sum.

❸ Shade the model to show the sum.

$$\frac{4}{10} + \frac{5}{10} = \frac{\boxed{4} + \square}{10} = \frac{\square}{\square}$$

B You can use models to help you subtract fractions.

 Subtract $\frac{5}{6} - \frac{3}{6}$.

> I'll shade the first fraction on the model. Then I'll cross out the parts that are being subtracted.

1 Subtract the numerators. Write the denominator.

2 Write the difference.

3 Shade the model to show the difference.

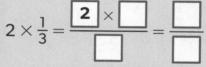

$$\frac{5}{6} - \frac{3}{6} = \frac{\boxed{5} - \square}{\square} = \frac{\square}{\square}$$

C You can use models to help you multiply a fraction by a whole number.

 Multiply $2 \times \frac{1}{3}$.

1 Multiply the whole number by the numerator of the fraction.

2 Write the denominator of the fraction as the denominator of the product.

3 Shade the model to show the product.

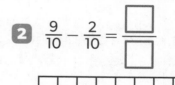

$$2 \times \frac{1}{3} = \frac{\boxed{2} \times \square}{\square} = \frac{\square}{\square}$$

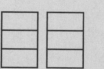

PRACTICE

Use the fraction models to help you add, subtract, or multiply.

1 $\frac{1}{4} + \frac{2}{4} = \dfrac{\square}{\square}$

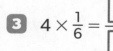

2 $\frac{9}{10} - \frac{2}{10} = \dfrac{\square}{\square}$

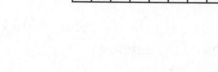

3 $4 \times \frac{1}{6} = \dfrac{\square}{\square}$

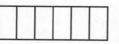

You can use **benchmarks** to estimate the weight of an object.

Think: A slice of bologna is about 1 ounce. A loaf of bread is about 1 pound.

Which is the better estimate of the weight of a puppy?

Use benchmarks to estimate the length of an object.

Think: The width of a pencil's eraser is about 1 centimeter. The length of a baseball bat is about 1 meter.

Which is the better estimate of the length of a pencil?

5 ounces ⟨ 5 pounds ⟩

⟨ 20 centimeters ⟩ 20 meters

A puppy weighs more than 5 slices of bologna, so 5 pounds is the better estimate.

A pencil is shorter than a baseball bat, so 20 centimeters is the better estimate.

Words to Know

benchmark
a measurement you can use to compare when estimating other measurements

 DISCUSS How can using a benchmark such as the length of a sheet of paper help you estimate the length of a table?

A You can use benchmarks to estimate customary capacities.

 DO Which is the better estimate of the capacity of the pitcher?

❶ Use benchmarks.

❷ Compare the benchmarks with the pitcher.

❸ Circle the better estimate.

2 cups

2 quarts

Think: A coffee mug is about 1 cup.
A milk carton is about 1 quart.

The pitcher is about _____ times as big as the milk carton.

B You can use benchmarks to estimate metric masses.

I can compare the masses of a postcard and textbook to an apple.

DO Which is the better estimate of the mass of an apple?

❶ Use benchmarks.

❷ Compare the benchmarks with the apple.

❸ Circle the better estimate.

100 grams   100 kilograms

Think: A postcard is about 1 gram.
    A math textbook is about 1 kilogram.

An apple is heavier than a _____, but lighter than a _____.

DISCUSS Ari says that the better estimate of the width of a soccer field is 75 inches, not 75 yards. Is Ari correct? If not, explain.

PRACTICE

Circle the better estimate.

❶

5 liters

5 milliliters

❷

3 gallons

3 cups

❸

8 ounces

8 pounds

❹

3 kilograms

3 grams

❺

25 centimeters

25 meters

❻

15 feet

15 yards

Carly bought $\frac{3}{4}$ pound of oven-roasted chicken and $\frac{3}{4}$ pound of barbecue chicken at the deli. How many pounds of chicken in all did Carly buy?

Write an equation.

Let p represent the total number of pounds of chicken.

$\frac{3}{4} + \frac{3}{4} = p$

Add. $\frac{3}{4} + \frac{3}{4} = \frac{3+3}{4} = \frac{6}{4}$

Change $\frac{6}{4}$ to a mixed number.

$\frac{6}{4} = \frac{4}{4} + \frac{2}{4} = 1 + \frac{2}{4} = 1\frac{2}{4}$

Carly bought $1\frac{2}{4}$ pounds of chicken.

Use models to check your answer.

OK! To add fractions that have the same denominator, I'll add the numerators, and keep the same denominator in the sum.

DISCUSS Explain how you can use estimation to check that your answer is reasonable to the problem above.

LESSON LINK

PLUG IN	POWER UP	GO!
Using models can help you add, subtract, and multiply fractions.	Using benchmarks can help you estimate the measurements of objects.	I see! I can use what I know about operations with fractions and measurement units to help me solve measurement word problems involving fractions.

$3 \times \frac{1}{8} = \frac{3}{8}$

2 cups   2 gallons

If your answer is an improper fraction, change it to a mixed number or whole number.

WORK TOGETHER

Write an equation to solve.

- The equation $\frac{1}{2} \times 4 = w$ represents the problem.

- Multiply to get $\frac{4}{2}$ as the product.

- Change $\frac{4}{2}$ to 2.

Monica pours 2 liters of water in all.

Monica pours $\frac{1}{2}$ liter of water into each of 4 containers. How much water does Monica pour in all?

Let w represent the amount of water Monica uses.

$\frac{1}{2}$ liter $\times$ 4 containers $= w$

$\frac{1}{2} \times 4 = \frac{1 \times 4}{2} = \frac{4}{2}$

$\frac{4}{2} = \frac{2}{2} + \frac{2}{2} = 1 + 1 = 2$

A Write an equation to solve.

 DO

Jane wants to put $\frac{3}{4}$ kilogram of rock salt into each of 5 paper bags. How much rock salt will Jane need?

❶ Write an equation. Let r represent the kilograms of rock salt Jane needs.

❷ Multiply.

❸ Change the product to a mixed number.

❹ Write the answer.

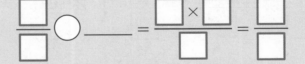

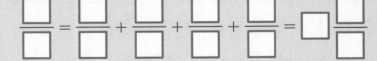

Jane will need _____ kilograms of rock salt.

DISCUSS

Nate plans to put fencing around his rectangular garden that measures $2\frac{1}{2}$ feet long by $3\frac{1}{2}$ feet wide. How many feet of fencing does Nate need to buy? Explain your answer.

I need to add the lengths of all 4 sides.

PRACTICE

Write an equation to solve.

1 Zoe filled 6 sandwich bags each with $\frac{1}{2}$ pound of peanut brittle. How much peanut brittle did Zoe use in all?

Let _____**p**_____ represent _____.

$$\underline{} \bigcirc \frac{\square}{\square} = p$$

$$6 \times \frac{\square}{\square} = \frac{\square \times \square}{\square} = \frac{\square}{\square} = \underline{}$$

> **HINT**
> You can use multiplication to find the total number.

Zoe used _____ pounds of peanut brittle.

2 Carson ran $\frac{5}{10}$ mile on Monday and $\frac{8}{10}$ mile on Tuesday. How far did Carson run on both days combined?

Let _____ represent _____.

$$\frac{\square}{\square} \bigcirc \frac{\square}{\square} = \underline{}$$

$$\frac{\square}{\square} \bigcirc \frac{\square}{\square} = \frac{\square + \square}{\square} = \frac{\square}{\square} = \square \frac{\square}{\square}$$

Carson ran _____ miles on Monday and Tuesday combined.

3 Elmer's Pass hiking trail is $\frac{7}{8}$ kilometers. Miller's Run hiking trail is $\frac{2}{8}$ kilometers shorter. How long is Miller's Run hiking trail?

The equation _____ represents the problem.

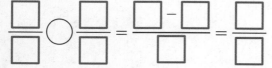

$$\frac{\square}{\square} \bigcirc \frac{\square}{\square} = \frac{\square - \square}{\square} = \frac{\square}{\square}$$

> **REMEMBER**
> The term "shorter" tells you to subtract.

Miller's Run hiking trail is _____ kilometers.

Solve. Show your work.

4 Julio has 10 minutes to run a mile. He completes it in $7\frac{1}{4}$ minutes. How much time is left?

_____ minutes

5 Fran spread $\frac{1}{3}$ tablespoon of peanut butter on each of 7 crackers. How many tablespoons of peanut butter did she use in all?

_____ tablespoons

I can use models to help me solve.

Solve.

6 Abby plans to fill 8 glasses each with $\frac{1}{2}$ cup of lemonade. How much lemonade will Abby need?

_____

7 Miguel walked $\frac{7}{8}$ kilometer on Friday, and $\frac{6}{8}$ kilometer on Saturday. How far did he walk over the two days?

_____

DISCUSS

Is It Correct?

Thomas turned in his math homework shown below.

Compare the factors to the product and the addends to the sum. Do they make sense?

1 $\frac{1}{5} \times 3 = \frac{1}{5 \times 3} = \frac{1}{15}$

2 $\frac{1}{3} \times 8 = \frac{1}{3 \times 8} = \frac{1}{24}$

3 $4 \times \frac{1}{10} = \frac{1}{4 \times 10} = \frac{1}{40}$

4 $\frac{3}{4} + \frac{2}{4} = \frac{5}{8}$

5 $\frac{4}{5} + \frac{1}{5} = \frac{5}{10}$

6 $\frac{5}{8} + \frac{7}{8} = \frac{12}{16}$

Did Thomas solve his homework problems correctly? Explain your answer.

PROBLEM SOLVING

PLACE YOUR ORDER

READ

Claire's Catering received an order for 6 appetizer platters. Each platter needs $\frac{7}{8}$ pound of cheese. How many pounds of cheese will Claire's Catering use to fill the order?

PLAN

• What is the problem asking you to find?

How many _____ of cheese will be used to fill the order?

• What do you need to know to solve the problem?

How many platters are in the order? _____

How many pounds of cheese are on one platter? _____

• How can you solve the problem?

You can use multiplication.

SOLVE

Write and solve a multiplication equation.

Let p represent the number of pounds of cheese.

$$\underline{\quad} \bigcirc \frac{\square}{\square} = p$$

$$\underline{\quad} \times \frac{\square}{\square} = \frac{\square \times \square}{\square} = \frac{\square}{\square} = \square\frac{\square}{\square}$$

CHECK

Use repeated addition.

$$\frac{7}{8} + \underline{\quad} + \underline{\quad} + \underline{\quad} + \underline{\quad} + \underline{\quad} = \underline{\quad} = \underline{\quad}$$

Claire's Catering will use _____ pounds of cheese.

PRACTICE

Write an equation. Use the problem-solving steps to help you.

I remember!
1 hour = 60 minutes

1 Nick has a math class that is 45 minutes long and a science class that is 50 minutes long. It takes 10 minutes to get from math to science. How much time passed from the beginning of math class to the end of science class?

CHECKLIST
- READ
- PLAN
- SOLVE
- CHECK

2 Rob has 10 glass jars. He will fill each with $\frac{1}{4}$ pound of beach sand for a project. How much sand will Rob use?

CHECKLIST
- READ
- PLAN
- SOLVE
- CHECK

3 Mary walks $\frac{8}{10}$ km round trip to school each day, Monday through Friday. What is the total distance Mary walks to and from school?

CHECKLIST
- READ
- PLAN
- SOLVE
- CHECK

16 Converting Units of Measurement to Solve Problems

PLUG IN Multiplying Whole Numbers

You can use repeated addition to help you multiply 3 × 350.

$$
\begin{array}{r}
1 \\
350 \\
\times\ 3 \\
\hline
1{,}050
\end{array}
\qquad
\begin{array}{r}
1 \\
350 \\
350 \\
+\ 350 \\
\hline
1{,}050
\end{array}
$$

The **product** is 1,050.

The **sum** is 1,050.

> I see! 3 × 350 is the same as adding 3 groups of 350.

The area model shows 12 × 11.

Separate the model into two parts.

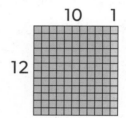

12 rows of 10: 12 × 10 = 120
12 rows of 1: 12 × 1 = 12
Add: 120 + 12 = 132

> I see! 12 × 11 = 12 × (10 + 1) = 132.

Words to Know

sum
the answer in an addition problem

product
the answer in a multiplication problem

 DISCUSS Will the product of 13 × 4 be the same as the product of 4 × 13? How would you use a model to answer this question?

A You can use repeated addition to help you multiply numbers.

 DO Multiply 1,313 × 4.

1. Set up multiplication problem. Find the product.

2. Use repeated addition to check your product.

3. Write the product.

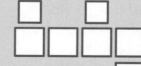

$$
\begin{array}{r}
\square\ \square \\
\square\ \square\ \square\ \square \\
\times\qquad\quad \boxed{4} \\
\hline
\square\ \square\ \square\ \square
\end{array}
$$

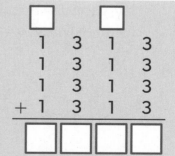

$$
\begin{array}{r}
\square\qquad\quad \square \\
1\ 3\ 1\ 3 \\
1\ 3\ 1\ 3 \\
1\ 3\ 1\ 3 \\
+\ 1\ 3\ 1\ 3 \\
\hline
\square\ \square\ \square\ \square
\end{array}
$$

1,313 × 4 = _____

B You can use an area model to multiply two 2-digit numbers.

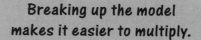
Breaking up the model makes it easier to multiply.

DO Multiply 13 × 10.

① Separate the model into two parts.

② Find the number of squares in each part.

③ Add to find the total.

④ Write the product.

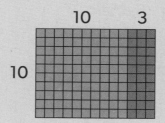

$10 \times 10 = \underline{\hspace{1cm}}$ $10 \times \underline{\hspace{1cm}} = \underline{\hspace{1cm}}$

$\underline{\hspace{1cm}} + \underline{\hspace{1cm}} = \underline{\hspace{1cm}}$

$13 \times 10 = \underline{\hspace{1cm}}$

PRACTICE

Find the product. Use repeated addition to help you.

1 $245 \times 3 = \underline{\hspace{1cm}}$

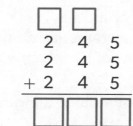

2 $8,000 \times 4 = \underline{\hspace{2cm}}$

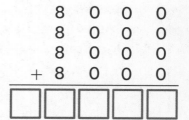

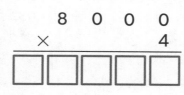

Use the area model to find the product.

3 $13 \times 15 = \underline{\hspace{1cm}}$

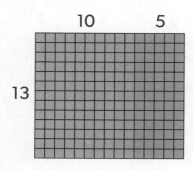

$13 \times \underline{\textbf{10}} = \underline{\hspace{1cm}}$

$13 \times \underline{\hspace{1cm}} = \underline{\hspace{1cm}}$

$\underline{\hspace{1cm}} + \underline{\hspace{1cm}} = \underline{\hspace{1cm}}$

You can use multiplication to convert a larger unit to a smaller unit.

Customary System

How many ounces are in 3 pounds?

1 pound (lb) = 16 ounces (oz)

3×16 oz = 48 oz

$16 + 16 + 16 = 48$ oz

There are 48 ounces in 3 pounds.

 I can use repeated addition to check the product.

You can use a table to help you convert measurements.

Metric System

How many centimeters are in 4 meters?

1 meter (m) = 100 centimeters (cm)

Meters	Centimeters
1	100
2	200
3	300
4	400

There are 400 centimeters in 4 meters.

When I convert metric units, I multiply by 10, 100, or 1,000.

 Words to Know

customary system
the measurement system used in the United States

    inches, pounds, quarts

metric system
the measurement system based on multiples of 10, which is used in most of the world

    centimeters, kilograms, liters

DISCUSS Why is it useful to have units of different sizes? Give an example.

A You can use multiplication to convert from hours to minutes.

DO How many minutes are in 3 hours?

❶ Write how many minutes are in 1 hour.

❷ Multiply to convert from a larger unit to a smaller unit.

❸ Write the minutes.

1 hour = __**60**__ minutes

$3 \times$ _____ = _____ minutes

There are _____ minutes in 3 hours.

 **Customary Units** can be found on p. 265.

B You can make a table to show equivalent measures.

> I know! Capacity means how much a container can hold.

DO Complete the table to show equivalent measures of capacity.

❶ Write how many quarts are equal to 1 gallon.

❷ Multiply to convert gallons to quarts.

❸ Complete the table.

1 gallon = __**4**__ quarts

Gallons	Quarts
1	
2	
3	
4	

DISCUSS Jason has 7 pounds of meat. He needs 120 ounces of meat for a barbeque. Does he have enough? Explain how you know.

> **Customary Units** and **Metric Units** can be found on pp. 265 and 267.

PRACTICE

Multiply to convert the units.

❶ How many minutes are in 5 hours?

1 hour = __**60**__ minutes

5 × _____ = _____ minutes

❷ How many milliliters are in 3 liters?

1 liter = _____ milliliters

_____ × _____ = _____ milliliters

Convert the units to complete the table.

❸

Feet	Inches
1	
2	
3	
4	

❹

Kilograms	Grams
1	
2	
5	
9	

Converting Units of Measurement to Solve Problems

You can use what you know about converting units to solve real-world measurement problems.

Ian bought 2 pounds of turkey and 6 ounces of cheese. How many total ounces of food did he buy?

I need to find how many ounces there are in 2 pounds and 6 ounces.

Find the number of ounces in 2 pounds of turkey.

Multiply to convert from pounds to ounces.

1 pound = 16 ounces

2 × 16 oz = 32 oz

2 pounds = 32 ounces.

Ian bought 32 oz of turkey.

Find the total number of ounces of food.

Add the numbers of ounces of turkey and cheese.

$$\begin{array}{r} 32 \text{ ounces} \\ +\quad 6 \text{ ounces} \\ \hline 38 \text{ ounces} \end{array}$$

I got it! Ian bought a total of 38 ounces of food.

DISCUSS

How would you find a total distance in meters if you were given a distance in kilometers and a distance in meters?

LESSON LINK

PLUG IN

You can use repeated addition to help you multiply.

3 × 12 = 36
12 + 12 + 12 = 36

POWER UP

You can multiply to convert a larger unit to a smaller unit.

1 foot = 12 inches
3 × 12 in. = 36 in.
3 feet = 36 inches

GO!

I get it! I can use multiplication to help me solve real-world problems that involve converting units of measurement.

> I have to first find how many meters equal 1 kilometer.

WORK TOGETHER

Convert units to solve a problem with measurement units.

- Ben walked 7 kilometers
- Multiply to find that 7 kilometers equal to 7,000 meters.

Ben walked 7,000 meters in all.

Ben walked 2 kilometers on Monday, 3 kilometers on Wednesday, and 2 kilometers on Saturday. How many meters did Ben walk in all?

$2 + 3 + 2 = 7$ kilometers

1 kilometer = 1,000 meters

$7 \times 1,000 = 7,000$ meters

> Customary Units can be found on p. 265.

A Convert units to solve.

 Seth mixes 2 gallons of orange juice with 1 quart of pineapple juice. How many quarts of juice does he have?

① Convert 2 gallons to quarts.

② Add 1 quart to the total.

③ Write the answer.

1 gallon = _____ quarts

$2 \times$ _____ = _____ quarts

_____ + _____ = _____ quarts

Seth has _____ quarts of juice.

B Convert units to solve.

 Jo made a paper chain 1 foot long. She added 3 inches to it. She finished the chain by adding another 3 feet. How many inches long was her chain?

① Find the total number of feet.

② Convert feet to inches.

③ Add 3 inches to the total.

④ Write the answer.

_____ + _____ = _____ feet

1 foot = _____ inches

_____ $\times$ _____ = _____ inches

_____ + _____ = _____ inches

Jo's paper chain was _____ inches long.

 Martin has a rope that is 8 feet long. He cuts the rope into 4 equal pieces. How many inches long is each piece?

> I can convert feet to inches by multiplying the number of feet by 12.

PRACTICE

Write the equivalent units. Convert units to solve.

Customary Units and Metric Units can be found on pp. 265 and 267.

1 Mrs. Winters bought a 4-pound chicken. How many ounces is the chicken?

1 pound = _____ ounces

_____ ounces

2 Rebecca bought 6 yards of fabric to make pillows. How many feet of fabric did she buy?

1 yard = __**3**__ feet

REMEMBER Multiply the number of yards by the number of feet in 1 yard.

_____ feet

3 Blake's baby brother weighs 10 kilograms. How many grams does the baby weigh?

1 kilogram = _____ grams

_____ grams

4 Anna mixed 575 milliliters of orange juice with 3 liters of pineapple juice in a large punch bowl. How many milliliters of juice in all did she mix?

1 liter = _____ milliliters

_____ milliliters

5 Tia babysat for 1 hour and 15 minutes, and Jasmine babysat for 3 hours and 45 minutes. How many minutes did both girls babysit in all?

1 hour = _____ minutes

_____ minutes

Solve. Show your work.

6 Joseph ran 2 kilometers. Jerry ran 200 meters less than Joseph. How many meters did they run in all?

7 It took 5 minutes and 35 seconds to download a large file onto Cindy's computer. How many seconds did the download take?

Customary Units and Metric Units can be found on pp. 265 and 267.

Solve.

8 Ling has a bag of gumballs. She plans to divide it among 5 friends. If the bag weighs 2 kilograms, how many grams of gumballs does each friend get?

_____

I need to use multiplication to convert larger units to smaller units.

9 Luis and Ken are building a track that is 5 meters long. So far, they have built 345 centimeters of the track. How many more centimeters do they have left to build?

_____

DISCUSS

Compare Using >, =, or <.

1 foot ◯ 14 inches

5 minutes ◯ 250 seconds

2 gallons ◯ 7 quarts

2 liters ◯ 2,000 milliliters

How did you do the conversions?

First find how many of the smaller unit equal 1 of the larger unit.

PROBLEM SOLVING

MAKING SOUP

READ

Janet is making soup. She has 2 kilograms of potatoes, 600 grams of carrots, 300 grams of celery, and 1 kilogram of chicken. What is the total mass, in grams, of all the ingredients?

PLAN

• What is the problem asking you to find?

The total number of _____ of soup ingredients

• What do you need to know to solve the problem?

1 kilogram = _____ grams

Janet is using _____ kilograms of potatoes,

_____ grams of carrots, _____ grams of celery, and

_____ kilogram of chicken.

SOLVE

Find the total mass in kilograms. Then convert to grams. Then add.

2 kilograms potatoes + 1 kilogram chicken = _____ kilograms

3 × _____ grams = _____ grams

_____ + _____ + _____ = _____ grams

CHECK

Convert the 2 kilograms of potatoes and 1 kilogram of chicken to grams.

There are _____ grams of potatoes and _____ grams of chicken. Add all the measurements in grams.

_____ + _____ + _____ + _____ = _____ grams

Janet will use a total of _____ grams of ingredients.

PRACTICE

Use the problem-solving steps to help you.

I remember! There are 60 minutes in 1 hour.

1 Isaiah slept for 8 hours and 25 minutes. How many minutes did he sleep?

CHECKLIST
- [ ] READ
- [ ] PLAN
- [ ] SOLVE
- [ ] CHECK

2 At a party, Rowan poured 300 milliliters of punch into each of 4 glasses. There was 1 liter of punch left in the bowl. How many milliliters of punch were there in all?

CHECKLIST
- [ ] READ
- [ ] PLAN
- [ ] SOLVE
- [ ] CHECK

3 Dalton's snake is 2 feet long. Ella's snake is 15 inches long. How many inches longer is Dalton's snake?

CHECKLIST
- [ ] READ
- [ ] PLAN
- [ ] SOLVE
- [ ] CHECK

17 Perimeter and Area of Rectangles

PLUG IN Finding Perimeter of Rectangles

The **perimeter** of a **rectangle** or a **square** is the distance around the figure.

3 in.
1 in. [ ] 1 in.
3 in.

The abbreviation "in." means inches.

To find the perimeter, add the lengths of the sides.

$$3 + 1 + 3 + 1 = 8$$

The lengths of the sides are given in inches.

I get it! The perimeter of the rectangle is 8 inches.

 Words to Know

perimeter	rectangle	square
the distance around the outside of a closed plane figure	a figure with 2 pairs of opposite sides that are parallel, and opposite sides that are the same length	a rectangle with 4 equal sides

DISCUSS Sonja found the perimeter of this rectangle by adding $5 + 1 + 5$. She says the perimeter is 11 inches. Is she correct? Explain.

5 in.
1 in. [ ] 1 in.
5 in.

A You can add side lengths to find the perimeter.

DO Find the perimeter.

❶ Add the lengths of all 4 sides.

❷ Include the units in your answer.

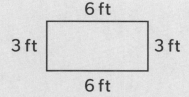

6 ft
3 ft [ ] 3 ft
6 ft

__6__ + __3__ + _____ + _____ = _____

The units for the lengths of the sides are in _____.

The perimeter of the rectangle is _____.

B You can find the perimeter of a rectangle if you know the lengths of two adjacent sides.

DO   Find the perimeter.

1 Opposite sides of a rectangle have the same length. Fill in the lengths of the missing sides.

2 Add the lengths.

3 Include the units in your answer.

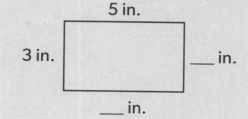

5 in.

3 in.   ___ in.

___ in.

__5__ + _____ + _____ + _____ = _____

The perimeter of the rectangle is _____.

C You can find the perimeter of a rectangle without a picture.

DO   A rectangular park is 2 miles long and 1 mile wide. What is the park's perimeter?

1 Find the lengths of the four sides.

2 Add the lengths.

3 Include the units in your answer.

Since opposite sides of a rectangle have __equal__ length, the other two sides have lengths of _____ and _____.

_____ + _____ + _____ + _____ = _____

The perimeter of the park is _____.

PRACTICE

Find the perimeter. Include the units in your answer.

1

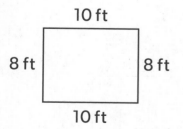

10 ft

8 ft   8 ft

10 ft

_____

2

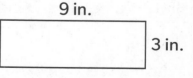

9 in.

3 in.

_____

3 A rectangular sports card has side lengths of 7 centimeters and 4 centimeters. What is the perimeter of the card?

_____

Finding Area of Rectangles

A **square unit** is a square with a side length of one unit.

1 cm □

This is 1 square centimeter.

To find the **area (A)** of a rectangle, find the number of square units that cover it.

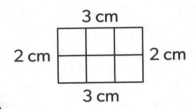
3 cm
2 cm   2 cm
3 cm

The area of the rectangle is 6 square centimeters.

You can also use a **formula** to find the area.

Area = length × width

$A = l \times w$

$A = 3 \times 2$

$A = 6$ square centimeters

I count 6 squares inside the rectangle.

I got the same answer when I multiplied as I did when I counted!

Words to Know

square unit
a unit used to measure the area of a figure

formula
an equation that represents a mathematical relationship

area
the number of square units that can cover the inside of a plane figure

---

DISCUSS How would you find the area of a rectangle with a length of 5 feet and a width of 3 feet? What units would you use in your answer?

A You can find the area of a rectangle by counting square units.

DO Find the area.

❶ Count the number of squares inside the rectangle.

❷ Write the area in square units.

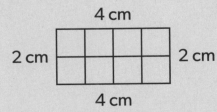
4 cm
2 cm   2 cm
4 cm

There are ___8___ squares inside the rectangle.

The area is _____.

B You can find the area of a rectangle by using a formula.

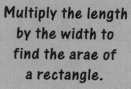
Multiply the length by the width to find the arae of a rectangle.

DO Find the area.

❶ Write the formula.

❷ Find the length and width of the rectangle.

❸ Write the values in the formula and multiply.

❹ Write the area in square units.

6 m

4 m

$A =$ ___*l*___ × _____

The length of this rectangle is _____ meters

and the width is _____ meters.

$A =$ _____ × _____ = _____

The area is _____.

DISCUSS Can you find the area of a square if you only know the length of 1 side? Explain.

PRACTICE

Use the model to find the area. Include the units in your answer.

1   4 in.

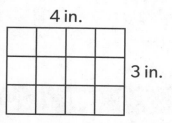   3 in.

_____

2   5 ft

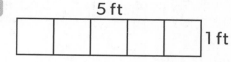   1 ft

_____

Find the area using the formula. Include the units in your answer.

3

5 m

8 m

_____

4   9 cm

3 cm

_____

You can use what you know about perimeter and area to solve problems.

Johann is building a wooden rectangle to use as a sandbox. It will be 4 feet long and 3 feet wide. How many feet of wood should Johann buy?

Since opposite sides of a rectangle are the same length, you can find the lengths of all four sides.

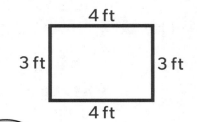

4 ft

3 ft 3 ft

4 ft

Add the lengths of the sides to find the perimeter.

$$3 + 4 + 3 + 4 = 14$$

Johann needs 14 feet of wood to build his sandbox.

Think: The amount of wood he needs is equal to the perimeter of the rectangle.

Sometimes it helps to draw a diagram of the problem.

I know! The length and width are given in feet, so the answer must also be in feet.

DISCUSS Cyril is buying paint for a wall that is 6 feet long and 8 feet high. How could you find the area of the wall? What is the area?

LESSON LINK

PLUG IN

The perimeter of a rectangle is equal to the sum of its four side lengths.

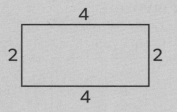

4

2 2

4

perimeter = 4 + 2 + 4 + 2
perimeter = 12 units

POWER UP

The area of a rectangle is equal to the product of its length and its width.

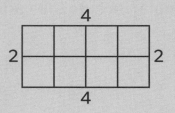

4

2 2

4

area = 4 × 2
area = 8 square units

GO!

I get it! I can use what I know about finding the perimeter and area of rectangles to solve real-world problems.

WORK TOGETHER

Use what you know about area to solve this problem.

- Make a diagram.

- Use the formula for area of a rectangle.

- Fill in 80 for area and 10 for the length in the formula.

- Use basic facts to find that $w = 8$.

The width of the picture frame is 8 inches.

A picture frame has an area of 80 square inches. It is 10 inches long. What is the frame's width?

10 in.

$A = 80$ sq in.

$A = l \times w$

$80 = 10 \times w$

Think: $10 \times ? = 80$

Since $10 \times 8 = 80$, $w = 8$.

Remember to use the correct units for the area.

A Use what you know about perimeter to solve the problem.

DO

Carla wants to sew ribbon around the edges of a square scarf with side lengths of 12 inches. How many inches of ribbon does she need?

1 Draw a diagram. Fill in the side lengths.

2 Find the perimeter.

3 Write the correct units in your answer.

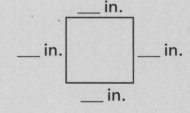

___ in.

___ in.   ___ in.

___ in.

_____ + _____ + _____ + _____ = _____

Carla needs _____ of ribbon.

DISCUSS

Sheila painted a canvas with an area of 64 square inches. She said that the canvas is square and that the side length is 7 inches. Can this be true? Explain.

A square has four equal sides, so I multiply the side length by itself to find the area.

PRACTICE

Fill in the diagram. Use what you know about perimeter and area to solve the problem. Include the units in your answer.

1 The fence around a garden is 10 feet long and 7 feet wide. How many feet of fencing make up the fence?

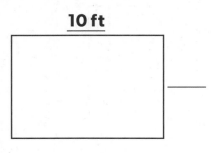

10 ft

2 A rectangular banner measures 5 yards by 2 yards. What is the area of the banner?

3 A book cover has an area of 54 square inches. It is 6 inches wide. What is the length of the book?

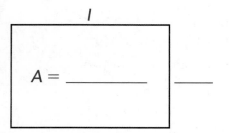

l

$A =$ _____

Find the missing measure. Include the units in your answer.

4

5 mi

A = 30 sq mi | w

w = _____

5

l

A = 56 sq ft | 8 ft

l = _____

6

l

A = 28 sq cm | 4 cm

l = _____

7

7 km

A = 49 sq km | w

w = _____

Solve.

I know! Since the length and width of a square are the same, I multiply the side length by itself to find the area.

8 Helmut is putting carpet in his living room, which measures 15 feet by 20 feet. How many square feet of carpeting does he need?

_____

9 The area of a square sticky note is 9 square inches. What are the length and width of the sticky note?

_____

DISCUSS **See the Relationship**

Bridgette wants to find the width of a rectangle.

She knows that the area of the rectangle is 21 square meters and the length is 7 meters.

How can she find the width of the rectangle?

What is the rectangle's width?

I remember! I can use the area formula and fill in the given values. Then I can find the missing value.

PROBLEM SOLVING

HOME IMPROVEMENT

READ Sanjay will tile the floor of his closet with square tiles that are 1 foot on each side. The closet is 5 feet by 3 feet. How many tiles will Sanjay need?

PLAN
- What is the problem asking you to find?

    The number of _____ Sanjay needs

- What do you need to know to solve the problem?

    The length is _____ and the width is _____.

    Each square tile has a side length of _____, so it covers 1 square foot.

- How can you solve the problem?

    You can use the formula $A =$ _____ to find the area.

SOLVE Fill in the length and width in the formula. Multiply.

$A =$ _____ $\times$ _____ $=$ _____

It will take _____ tiles to cover it the closet.

CHECK Make a diagram.

Divide a rectangle into 5 equal columns and 3 equal rows.

5 feet

3 feet

The rectangle shows _____ equal squares.

Each square represents 1 _____.

Sanjay will need _____ tiles for his closet.

The formula for the area of a rectangle is $A = l \times w$.

PRACTICE

Use the problem-solving steps to help you. Include the units in your answer.

1 A quilt is made up of squares of cloth stitched together. Each square of cloth has a side length of 1 foot. How many cloth squares are needed to sew a quilt that is 10 feet by 6 feet?

CHECKLIST
- [ ] READ
- [ ] PLAN
- [ ] SOLVE
- [ ] CHECK

2 A travel chess set has a board made up of 1-inch by 1-inch squares. If there are 8 squares on each edge of the board, what is the area of the chess board?

CHECKLIST
- [ ] READ
- [ ] PLAN
- [ ] SOLVE
- [ ] CHECK

3 Mai-An is painting a checkerboard pattern onto her walls. Each square that makes up the pattern has a side length of 1 foot. How many squares will she need to paint to cover a wall that is 10 feet by 9 feet?

CHECKLIST
- [ ] READ
- [ ] PLAN
- [ ] SOLVE
- [ ] CHECK

PLUG IN | **Understanding Customary and Metric Units of Measure**

These are examples of units of measurement.

- length: inches (in.), feet (ft), centimeters (cm), meters (m)

- weight and **mass:** ounces (oz), pounds (lb), grams (g), kilograms (kg)

- **capacity** (liquid volume): quarts (qt), gallons (gal), milliliters (mL), and liters (L)

The picture shows some measurement tools.

Words to Know

capacity (liquid volume)
the amount of liquid that a container can hold

mass
the amount of matter in an object

 DISCUSS There are 16 ounces in 1 pound. Discuss how you can find how many ounces are in $\frac{1}{2}$ pound.

A You can estimate the length of an object.

 DO What is the best estimate for the length of a pencil: $\frac{1}{2}$ inch, $\frac{1}{2}$ foot, or $\frac{1}{2}$ yard?

❶ Think about the length of a sheet of paper.

❷ Compare the length of the sheet of paper to the pencil.

❸ Write the best estimate.

A sheet of notebook paper is about

___12___ inches or _____ foot long.

The pencil is about _____ the length of the sheet of paper.

The best estimate for the length of the pencil

is _____.

B You can choose the better estimate of capacity.

1 milliliter is about how much water is in a raindrop.

DO Does a drinking glass hold $\frac{1}{2}$ liter or $\frac{1}{2}$ milliliter of water?

1 Compare the size of each unit of capacity.

2 Write the better estimate.

The capacity of the drinking glass is _____ than 1 liter.

The capacity of the drinking glass is _____ than 1 milliliter.

The drinking glass holds about _____ of water.

PRACTICE

Circle the better estimate for each measure.

1 the mass of a dog

50 milligrams   50 kilograms

2 the capacity of a water bottle

4 cups   4 gallons

3 the length of a jump rope

2 meters   2 millimeters

4 the weight of a letter

1 pound   1 ounce

POWER UP · Adding and Subtracting Fractions

You can draw a model to help you add or subtract fractions with the same **denominator**.

Add the **numerators**. The denominator stays the same.

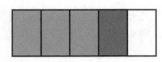

$$\frac{3}{5} + \frac{1}{5} = \frac{3+1}{5} = \frac{4}{5}$$

I get it! The total shaded parts show the sum.

Subtract the numerators. Keep the denominator.

$$\frac{4}{5} - \frac{1}{5} = \frac{4-1}{5} = \frac{3}{5}$$

Since the denominators are the same, I just add or subtract the numerators.

 Words to Know

denominator
the bottom number in a fraction that tells the number of parts in the whole

numerator
the top number in a fraction that tells how many equal parts are being counted

DISCUSS Dylan says his model shows $\frac{5}{6} - \frac{3}{6} = \frac{2}{6}$. What would you say to Dylan about his model?

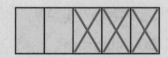

A You can use a fraction model to add fractions.

DO Add $\frac{1}{6} + \frac{4}{6}$.

❶ The denominator is 6, so divide the model in sixths.

❷ Shade the model to show $\frac{1}{6}$. Then shade $\frac{4}{6}$ more.

❸ Count the total shaded parts.

❹ Write the sum.

$$\frac{1}{6} + \frac{4}{6} = \frac{\Box}{\Box}$$

The denominator stays the same.

B You can use a fraction model to subtract fractions.

DO Subtract $\frac{3}{4} - \frac{1}{4}$.

❶ Make a model to show $\frac{3}{4}$.

❷ Cross out $\frac{1}{4}$.

❸ Count the number of $\frac{1}{4}$ parts that are left.

❹ Write the difference.

| $\frac{1}{4}$ | $\frac{1}{4}$ | $\frac{1}{4}$ | |

$$\frac{3}{4} - \frac{1}{4} = \frac{\square}{\square}$$

C You can add or subtract fractions without using a model.

DO Add $\frac{3}{10} + \frac{4}{10}$.

❶ Add the numerators.

❷ Keep the denominator.

$$\frac{3}{10} + \frac{4}{10} = \frac{\boxed{3} + \boxed{4}}{10} = \frac{\square}{\square}$$

DISCUSS Which model do you prefer for adding and subtracting fractions? Why?

PRACTICE

Use the models to help you add or subtract the fractions.

❶ $\frac{3}{8} + \frac{2}{8} = \frac{\square}{8}$

❷ $\frac{4}{6} - \frac{2}{6} = \frac{\square}{6}$

| $\frac{1}{6}$ | $\frac{1}{6}$ | $\frac{1}{6}$ | $\frac{1}{6}$ | |

Add or subtract.

❸ $\frac{5}{8} + \frac{2}{8} = \frac{\square}{8}$

❹ $\frac{3}{5} - \frac{2}{5} = \frac{\square}{5}$

❺ $\frac{1}{6} + \frac{4}{6} = \frac{\square}{\square}$

❻ $\frac{7}{10} - \frac{5}{10} = \frac{\square}{\square}$

Labeled Fraction Strips can be found on p. 259.

Lengths of Leaves (in inches)

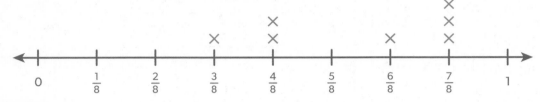

A **line plot** uses a number line to show a set of data values.

This line plot shows the lengths of some leaves.

The data values have measurement units.

These leaves were measured in inches.

Each X in the line plot represents one leaf.

The 3 Xs above $\frac{7}{8}$ show that there are 3 leaves that were each $\frac{7}{8}$ inch long.

Words to Know

line plot
a graph that uses Xs above a number line to show data

DISCUSS How can you find how many leaves in all were measured?

LESSON LINK

PLUG IN	POWER UP	GO!

The customary and metric systems have different measurement units.

Customary	Metric
inch (in.)	centimeter (cm)
foot (ft)	meter (m)
pounds (lb)	kilogram (kg)
quart (qt)	milliliter (mL)
gallon (gal)	liter (L)

Models can help you add and subtract fractions.

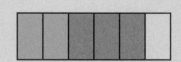

$$\frac{2}{6} + \frac{3}{6} = \frac{5}{6}$$

I get it! I can use what I know about measurement units and adding and subtracting fractions to solve problems with line plots.

WORK TOGETHER

Make a line plot to show the lengths of the ribbons in meters.

- The number line is labeled from 0 to 1 in tenths.
- Each X represents one ribbon.
- The title of the line plot includes the units.

The number of Xs on the line plot should be the same as the number of items in the data set.

Lengths of Ribbons (in meters):

$$\frac{1}{10}, \frac{3}{10}, \frac{3}{10}, \frac{4}{10}, \frac{6}{10}, \frac{7}{10}, \frac{7}{10}, \frac{8}{10}, \frac{8}{10}, \frac{8}{10}$$

Lengths of Ribbons (in meters)

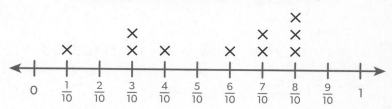

A You can solve problems using the data in a line plot.

DO Find the difference between the weights of the lightest and heaviest pencils.

1. Find the weight for the first X on the line plot.

2. Find the weight for the last X on the line plot.

3. Subtract the numerators. Keep the denominator.

4. Find the difference.

Weights of Pencils (in ounces)

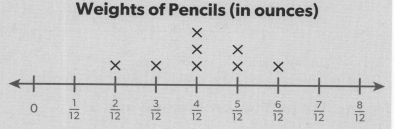

The lightest pencil weighs _____ ounce.

The heaviest pencil weighs _____ ounce.

$$\frac{\square}{12} - \frac{\square}{12} = \frac{\square - \square}{12} = \frac{\square}{12}$$

The difference is _____ ounces.

DISCUSS Jamal made a line plot showing the lengths of some leaves in his yard. How can Jamal find the shortest length on the line plot?

If there are no Xs above a number, that means there are no leaves for that length.

PRACTICE

Use the data for problems 1–3.

Masses of honeydew melons (in kilograms):

$$\frac{4}{10}, \frac{5}{10}, \frac{5}{10}, \frac{6}{10}, \frac{6}{10}, \frac{6}{10}, \frac{7}{10}$$

1 What is the unit of measurement for the honeydew melons?

_____

2 How many honeydew melons are included in the data set?

_____

3 Make a line plot to show the data.

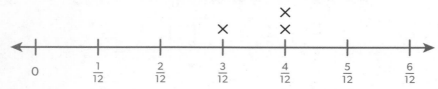

Use the line plot for problems 4 and 5.

The line plot shows the weights of some hamburgers Isaiah made.

Weights of Hamburgers (in pounds)

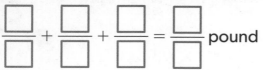

4 How many hamburgers did Isaiah make?

_____

5 What is the total weight of the hamburgers?

$$\frac{\Box}{\Box} + \frac{\Box}{\Box} + \frac{\Box}{\Box} = \frac{\Box}{\Box} \text{ pound}$$

Use the line plot for problems 6 and 7.

Lengths of Students' Strides (in yards)

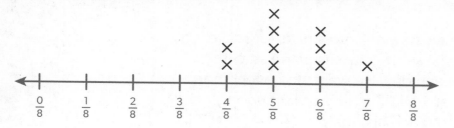

I can subtract to find the difference between data values.

6 How many students had stride lengths that were longer than $\frac{5}{8}$ yard? _____

7 What is the difference between the longest stride and the shortest stride? _____

DISCUSS

Analyze Data

Theresa made a line plot to show how far her classmates walk to school.

Distances Walked to School (in miles)

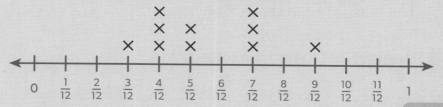

How many classmates walk $\frac{4}{12}$ mile to school?

How can you find the total distance walked by those classmates?

The words, "total distance" tell you the operations to use.

What is the total distance walked by those classmates?

PROBLEM SOLVING

STACKING UP

READ

Zachary ties newspapers into stacks for recycling. The line plot shows the masses of the stacks he collected each day. He wants to collect more than $\frac{9}{10}$ kilogram. Did Zachary collect enough newspapers to reach his goal?

Masses of Newspaper Stacks (in kilograms)

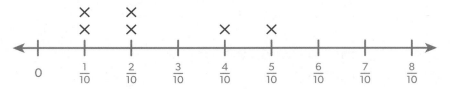

PLAN

• What is the problem asking you to find?

The total _____ of the newspapers

• What do you need to know to solve the problem?

The mass of each stack of newspapers

SOLVE

Add the fractions to find the total mass.

$$\frac{1}{10} + \frac{1}{10} + \frac{2}{10} + \frac{2}{10} + \frac{4}{10} + \frac{5}{10} = \frac{1 + 1 + 2 + 2 + 4 + 5}{10} = \frac{\boxed{}}{10}$$

Is the sum more than $\frac{9}{10}$ kg? _____

CHECK

Draw a model.

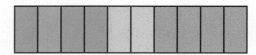
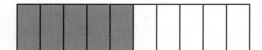

Zachary _____ collect enough newspapers to reach his goal.

PRACTICE

Use the problem-solving steps to help you.

1 The line plot shows the widths of the spines of Jayden's books. Find the total width of the books' spines, and tell whether the books will fit on a shelf that is one foot wide.

I remember! Each X represents 1 book.

Widths of Book Spines (in feet)

```
                  ×
          ×       ×
          ×       ×
          ×       ×       ×       ×
  ←───┼───┼───┼───┼───┼───┼───┼───→
      0   1/12 2/12 3/12 4/12 5/12 6/12
```

2 The line plot shows the amounts of red paint left over after art class. Is there more than 1 liter of red paint left?

Amount of Paint (in liters)

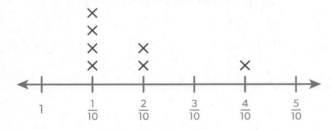

```
          ×
          ×
          ×       ×
          ×       ×               ×
  ←─┼───┼───┼───┼───┼───┼───→
    1  1/10 2/10 3/10 4/10 5/10
```

Solving Problems with Angle Measures

PLUG IN   Understanding Angles

An **angle** is formed where two **rays** meet at a **vertex**.

Vertex *A* is the **endpoint** of each of the two rays.

A

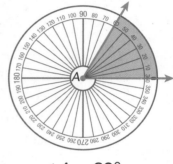

Point *A* is the vertex of the angle. The angle can be called angle *A*.

The vertex of angle *A* is at the center of the circle. One ray lines up with 0. The other ray lines up with the number that shows the angle's measure.

∠*A* = 60°

I see! The symbol ∠ stands for angle. Angle *A* has a measure of 60 degrees.

Words to Know	angle	ray	vertex	endpoint
	a figure formed where two rays meet at a vertex	a part of a line with an endpoint at one end	the point where two rays meet to form an angle	a point at the ends of a line segment or a ray

 The circle above is divided into 360 parts, or 360 degrees. What fraction of the circle does an angle of 1 degree represent?

A You can form and name an angle from two rays that meet at a point.

DO   Draw and name an angle.

1 Draw two rays that share an endpoint or vertex.

2 Name the vertex.

3 Name the angle.

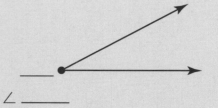

_____

∠ _____

B You can draw an angle as part of a circle.

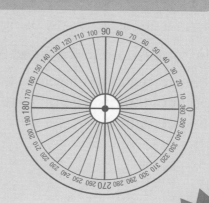

Two rays that meet at the center of a circle form an angle.

DO Draw an angle with a measure of 30°.

① Mark the angle's vertex in the center of the circle.

② From the vertex, draw a ray that lines up with 0.

③ From the vertex, draw another ray that lines up with 30.

PRACTICE

Draw angles. Name the vertex. Then name the angle.

1

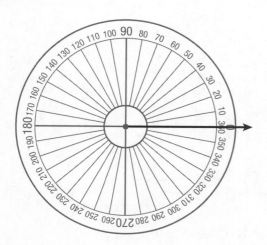

∠ ____

2

∠ ____

360° Circle can be found on p. 269.

Draw and label the given angle on the circle.

3 ∠G = 70°

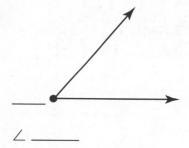

4 ∠B = 130°

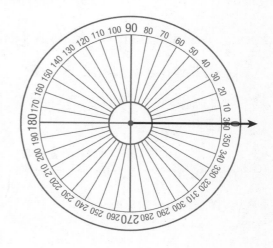

You can measure an angle by using a **protractor**.

An angle is measured in **degrees** (°).

Line up the vertex of the angle with the center point of the protractor. One ray should line up with 0.

The other ray lines up with 70 on the inner scale. This is a 70° angle.

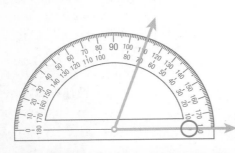

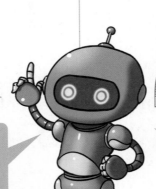

The ray lines up with 0 at the right of the protractor, so I need to read the inner scale.

The 70 is on the same scale as 0.

Words to Know

protractor	**degrees (°)**
a tool used to measure angles	the units used to measure angles

DISCUSS How are the two scales on a protractor different?

A You can measure an angle with a protractor.

DO Find the measure of ∠E.

❶ One ray is lined up with 0 on the outer scale.

❷ Find the number on the scale that the other ray lines up with.

❸ Write the measure of ∠E.

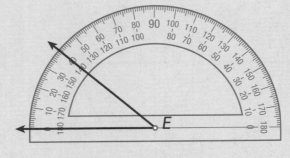

∠E has a measure of _____°.

B You can use a straightedge and a protractor to draw an angle.

The angle can open to the left or to the right.

DO Draw a 125° angle.

❶ Draw a ray with endpoint.

❷ Line up the endpoint and the 0° mark on the protractor with your ray.

❸ Make a dot at 125°.

❹ Draw a ray from the vertex to the 125° dot to form the angle.

DISCUSS In your drawing of the angle above, did you use the inner scale or the outer scale to draw the 125° angle? Explain.

PRACTICE

Use a protractor to measure the angle.

1

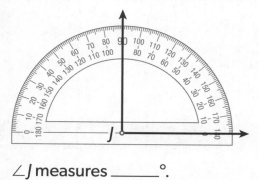

∠J measures _____°.

2

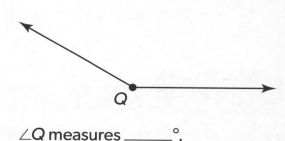

∠Q measures _____°.

Draw an angle with the given measure.

3 65°

4 118°

Solving Problems with Angle Measures

The two smaller angles form one larger angle.

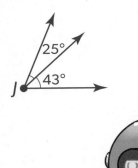

The two smaller angles share a vertex, J, and a ray.

You can find the measure of the larger angle by adding the measures of the smaller angles.

$25° + 43° = 68°$

I see! I can add degrees just like I add whole numbers.

An angle can be divided into two smaller angles.

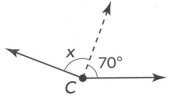

$\angle C$ is $158°$.

$158 - 70 = 88°$

I subtracted to find the measure of $\angle x$ to be $88°$.

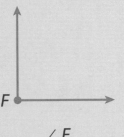

DISCUSS When would you use addition and when would you use subtraction to find missing angle measures?

LESSON LINK

PLUG IN ▶ **POWER UP** ▶ **GO!**

An angle is formed where two rays meet.

$\angle F$

You can use a protractor to measure an angle in degrees.

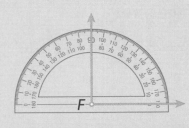

$\angle F$ has a measure of $90°$.

I get it! I can measure angles and use their degree measures to solve problems.

WORK TOGETHER

What is the measure of the angle shown by the hands of a clock when it is 4:00?

The hands of a clock form angles all day!

- At 3:00, the hands form a 90° angle.

- Each hour is a 30° angle.

The angle measure at 4:00 is 120°.

90° + 30° = 120°

A Use addition to find the measure of a larger angle.

DO Find the measure of ∠L.

1. Identify the two angles that form the larger angle.

2. Write an addition equation.

3. Add to find the measure of ∠L.

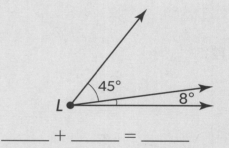

_____ + _____ = _____

The measure of ∠L is _____°.

B Use subtraction to find the measure of a smaller angle.

DO ∠S = 154°. Find the measure of angle x.

1. Identify the two angles that form the larger angle.

2. Write a subtraction equation.

3. Subtract to find the measure of x.

_____ − _____ = _____

The measure of ∠x is _____°.

DISCUSS How could you check to make sure your answer for the measure of the missing angle, x, is correct?

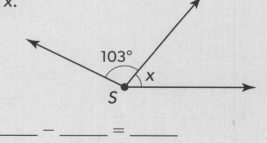

If you know two of the three angle measures, you can find the third!

PRACTICE

Find the missing angle measure.

1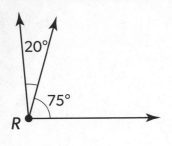

_____ + _____ = _____

∠R = _____ °

2 ∠C = 94°

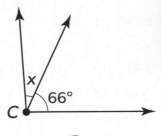

_____ ⊖ _____ = _____

∠x = _____ °

3 ∠F = 121°

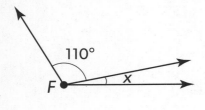

_____ ◯ _____ = _____

∠x = _____ °

4

_____ ◯ _____ = _____

∠Q = _____ °

5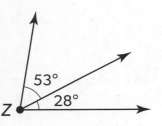

_____ ◯ _____ = _____

∠Z = _____ °

6 ∠T = 136°

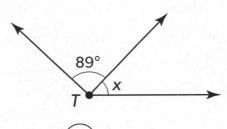

_____ ◯ _____ = _____

∠x = _____ °

Draw a model to help you solve the problem.

7 A large angle is made up of two smaller angles. The smaller angles measure 48° and 11°. What is the measure of the large angle?

8 A 165° angle is divided into two smaller angles. One of the smaller angles measures 90°. What is the measure of the other angle?

Solve.

9 Ben opens his desk 25° to get a pencil. Then he opens it another 55° to get a notebook. How far does Ben open his desk?

_____

10 Sarah's desk is open at 90°. She closes it 17° and pauses to answer a question. How much farther does she need to go until the desk is completely closed?

_____

I can draw a model to help me solve these problems!

DISCUSS

Model with Math

Think about fact families.

Diego wrote one equation to find a missing angle measure. Write three more equations to solve the same problem.

$$180° - \underline{\hspace{1cm}}° = 48°$$

_____

_____   _____

How do all four equations model the same problem?

PROBLEM SOLVING

SCHOOL TIME

READ
A clock's minute hand moves 60° in 10 minutes and 180° in 30 minutes. How far does it move from 11:00 to 11:40?

PLAN
• What is the problem asking you to find?

The measure of the angle on a clock from

_____ to _____

• What do you need to know to solve the problem?

What is the measure of the angle from 11:00 to 11:30? _____

What is the measure of the angle from 11:30 to 11:40? _____

• How can you find the missing angle measure?

You can use an equation.

SOLVE
Write an addition equation.

Angle from 11:00 to 11:30	+	Angle from 11:30 to 11:40	=	Angle from 11:00 to 11:40
_____	+	_____	=	_____

CHECK
Subtract to check the sum.

Angle from 11:00 to 11:40	−	Angle from 11:00 to 11:30	=	Angle from 11:30 to 11:40
_____	−	_____	=	_____

From 11:00 to 11:40, the minute hand moves _____°.

PRACTICE

I know! I can draw angles to help me solve the problem.

Use the problem-solving steps to help you.

1 An owl can turn its head about 180° in one direction. A robot can turn its head about 75°. How much farther would the robot have to turn its head to turn it as far as an owl can?

CHECKLIST
- [ ] READ
- [ ] PLAN
- [ ] SOLVE
- [ ] CHECK

2 The minute hand on a clock moves 30° from 2:00 to 2:05. Then it moves another 90°. What time is it?

CHECKLIST
- [ ] READ
- [ ] PLAN
- [ ] SOLVE
- [ ] CHECK

3 Nyla put two triangles together to make a parallelogram. The connecting angles of the triangles each measure 60°. What is the measure of the angle they form in the parallelogram?

CHECKLIST
- [ ] READ
- [ ] PLAN
- [ ] SOLVE
- [ ] CHECK

20 Classifying Two-Dimensional Figures

PLUG IN   Identifying Shapes

You can identify shapes by counting the numbers of angles and sides.

- Triangles have 3 angles and 3 sides.

- **Quadrilaterals** have 4 angles and 4 sides. A **square**, a **rectangle**, and a **rhombus** are all special kinds of quadrilaterals.

- Pentagons have 5 angles and 5 sides.

- Hexagons have 6 angles and 6 sides.

triangle

square

rectangle

rhombus

pentagon

hexagon

I see! Each shape has the same number of angles as number of sides.

 Words to Know

quadrilateral a two-dimentional figure with 4 sides	**square** a quadrilateral with 4 equal sides and 4 square corners	**rectangle** a quadrilateral with 4 square corners	**rhombus** a quadrilateral with 4 equal sides

DISCUSS   Nicole says that this shape is a quadrilateral. Hunter says that the shape is a square. Who is correct? Explain.

A You can identify shapes by counting the number of sides and angles.

DO   Name the shape.

❶ Write the number of sides.

❷ Write the number of angles.

❸ Name the shape.

___**3**___ sides

_____ angles

The shape is a _____.

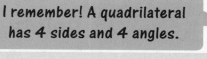

I remember! A quadrilateral has 4 sides and 4 angles.

B You can identify some shapes by more than one name.

DO   Name the shape in 2 ways.

❶ Count the number of sides. Describe the sides.

❷ Count the number of angles. Describe the angles.

❸ Name the shape in two ways.

The ___**4**___ sides _____ all the same length.

The _____ angles all form _____ corners.

The shape is a _____ and

a _____.

PRACTICE

Write the number of sides and angles. Identify the shape.

1

___**6**___ sides

_____ angles

_____

2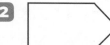

_____ sides

_____ angles

_____

3

_____ equal sides

_____ angles

_____

_____

4

_____ equal sides

_____ angles

_____

_____

Points, rays, lines, and angles make up figures.

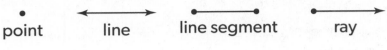

point   line   line segment   ray

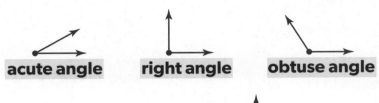

acute angle   **right angle**   **obtuse angle**

parallel lines   perpendicular lines

A rectangle has points, line segments, right angles, parallel lines, and perpendicular lines.

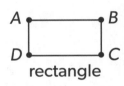

rectangle

> A right angle looks like a square corner formed by two lines, line segments, or rays.

Words to Know	**acute angle** an angle with a measure less than 90°	**right angle** an angle with a measure of 90°	**obtuse angle** an angle with a measure greater than 90° and less than 180°

DISCUSS Leah drew a straight mark connecting two points that are 3 inches apart. She says she drew a line. What can you tell Leah?

A You can draw line segments.

DO Complete the figure to make a 2-inch line segment.

1 Draw a point 2 inches away from the first point.

2 Draw a straight line between the 2 points.

B You can identify angles and line segments in figures.

 Identify the parts in this figure.

1 Write the angles.

2 Tell if the angles are acute, right, or obtuse.

3 Tell if any of the line segments are perpendicular or parallel.

Perpendicular line segments form square corners.

Angles ____**A**____, _____, _____, _____.

The angles are all _____ angles.

The red and blue sides are _____.

The blue and green sides are _____.

 Jake draws a square on a piece of paper. He wants to draw a bigger square on the board. Will Jake need to draw bigger sides or bigger angles?

PRACTICE

Draw an example of the figure on the grid.

Grid Paper can be found on p. 231.

1 a right angle

2 perpendicular line segments

Identify the angles and line segments in the figure.

3

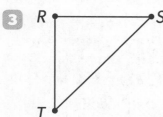

angles _____, _____, _____

types of angles

_____ and _____

type of line segments

_____

A figure can be classified by the measures of its angles and whether or not it has parallel or perpendicular sides.

Figure A

① Figure A has four right angles.

Figure B has one right angle and two acute angles.

② Figure A has parallel and perpendicular sides.

Figure B has perpendicular sides.

③ Figure A is a square.

Figure B is a **right triangle**.

Figure B

I can use what I know about line segments and angles to classify figures.

Words to Know

right triangle
a triangle with one right angle

DISCUSS Lucas says a triangle can have two right angles. What can you tell Lucas?

LESSON LINK

PLUG IN · **POWER UP** · **GO!**

You can identify a figure by the number of angles and sides it has.

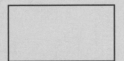

There are 4 sides and 4 angles that are square corners. This is a quadrilateral and a rectangle.

You can identify angles and parallel and perpendicular line segments in figures.

A rectangle has right angles and parallel and perpendicular line segments.

I get it! I can use what I know about angles and sides to help me classify figures.

I can look for special angles and sides.

WORK TOGETHER

You can sort figures based on their sides and angles.

- All the figures have 4 sides. So they are all quadrilaterals.

- Figures with opposite sides that stay the same distance apart have parallel sides.

- Figures with sides that form square corners have perpendicular sides.

- A square and a rhombus have 4 equal sides.

Quadrilaterals		
parallel sides	**perpendicular sides**	**4 equal sides**
trapezoid rectangle	rectangle	square
parallelogram	square	rhombus
square rhombus		

A Use Math Tool: Two-Dimensional Figures.

DO Draw and label the figures with at least one right angle.

1 Find the figures with square corners.

2 Draw and label each figure.

Two-Dimensional Figures can be found on p. 271.

B Use Math Tool: Two-Dimensional Figures.

DO Draw and label the figures with perpendicular sides.

1 Find the figures with sides that meet at a right angle.

2 Draw and label each figure.

DISCUSS Peyton says that if a figure has perpendicular sides, it will also have a right angle. Is Peyton correct? Explain.

I can draw a model to help me see the figure.

PRACTICE

Use Math Tool: Two-Dimensional Figures.
Draw and label the figures that fit each description.

Two-Dimensional Figures can be found on p. 271.

1 at least one obtuse angle

rhombus

HINT
An obtuse angle is greater than 90°.

2 at least one pair of parallel sides

rectangle

REMEMBER
Parallel sides stay the same distance apart.

List all the quadrilaterals that fit the description.

rhombus   square   parallelogram   trapezoid   rectangle

3 four right angles

_____

4 two pairs of perpendicular sides

_____

5 only one pair of parallel sides

_____

6 two acute angles

_____

7 two obtuse angles

_____

8 two pairs of parallel sides

_____

Solve.

9 I have three pairs of parallel sides and six obtuse angles. Which figure am I?

_____

Right angles are 90°. Obtuse angles are greater than 90°.

10 I have four right angles and two pairs of parallel sides. Each of my sides is the same length. Which figure am I?

_____

Check the Reasoning

Dominic says a rhombus and a square are always alike. He wrote his reasoning.

A right angle makes a square corner.

A rhombus and a square always have four right angles and two pairs of equal sides.

Is Dominic correct? Explain why or why not.

PROBLEM SOLVING

FIGURE IT OUT

READ Faith has a set of quadrilaterals to sort for homework. She has to circle all of the parallelograms. Draw and name all of the figures Faith should circle.

Set of Quadrilaterals

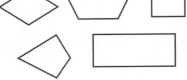

PLAN • What is the problem asking you to do?

Draw and name the _____ that Faith should circle.

• What do you need to know to solve the problem?

A parallelogram is _____

_____

• How can you determine which figures Faith should circle?

I can use what I know about parallelograms to draw and identify the figures.

SOLVE Draw and name the figures.

Parallelograms have two pairs of equal parallel sides.

CHECK Compare your figures with the definition of a parallelogram.

All of my figures have two pairs of parallel sides and equal opposite sides.

Faith should circle the _____, _____, _____, and the _____.

PRACTICE

I will use the sides and angles to identify each figure.

Use the problem-solving steps to help you.

1 Liam draws a figure on his paper. It has two right angles and five sides. What figure did Liam draw?

CHECKLIST
- [ ] READ
- [ ] PLAN
- [ ] SOLVE
- [ ] CHECK

2 Owen draws a quadrilateral with two acute angles, two obtuse angles, and one pair of parallel sides. What quadrilateral did Owen draw?

CHECKLIST
- [ ] READ
- [ ] PLAN
- [ ] SOLVE
- [ ] CHECK

3 Rebecca drew three different quadrilaterals. Each quadrilateral has four right angles and two pairs of parallel sides. What three quadrilaterals could Rebecca have drawn?

CHECKLIST
- [ ] READ
- [ ] PLAN
- [ ] SOLVE
- [ ] CHECK

Glossary

acute angle an angle with a measure less than 90° (Lesson 20)

add to find the total when two or more values are joined (Lesson 2)

$$100 + 25 = 125$$

addend a number to be added (Lesson 4)

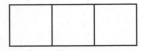

$$6 + 6 = 12$$
addends

angle a figure that is formed when two rays meet at one point called a vertex (Lesson 19)

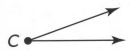

C

area the number of squares having a side length of 1 unit that can completely cover the inside of a plane figure with no gaps or overlaps (Lesson 17)

area = 3 square units

associative property the rule that states that the order in which you group numbers does not matter (Lesson 7)

$$(17 + 22) + 34 = 17 + (22 + 34)$$

benchmark a measurement you can use to compare when estimating other measurements (Lesson 15)

capacity the amount of liquid that a container can hold (Lesson 18)

commutative property the rule that states that the order in which you add two numbers does not change the sum (Lesson 7)

$$28 + 10 = 10 + 28$$

composite number a whole number that has more than one factor pair (Lesson 3)

4 is a composite number.

common denominator a common multiple of the denominators of two or more fractions (Lesson 11)

A common denominator for $\frac{1}{3}$ and $\frac{1}{5}$ is 15.

customary system the system of measurement units used in the United States (Lesson 16)

decimal a number with one or more digits to the right of a decimal point (Lesson 14)

1.23 is a decimal. There are two digits to the right of the decimal point.

decimal point a period separating the ones from the tenths in a decimal (Lesson 14)

$$1.23$$
↑
decimal point

degree(°) a unit for measuring angles (Lesson 19)

denominator the bottom number in a fraction that tells how many equal parts in the whole or group (Lessons 10, 11, 18)

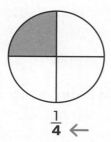

$$\frac{1}{4} \leftarrow$$

difference the answer in a subtraction problem (Lesson 12)

$$82 - 50 = \mathbf{32}$$
↑
difference

digit any of the numerals 0, 1, 2, 3, 4, 5, 6, 7, 8, and 9 (Lessons 5, 6)

distributive property the rule that states that multiplying a sum by a number is the same as multiplying each addend separately and then adding the products (Lesson 8)

dividend the number to be divided (Lesson 9)

$$4\overline{)160}$$ with quotient 40
↑
dividend

divisible able to be divided by a number (Lesson 4)

15 is divisible by 5.

division fact a basic fact that has a dividend, a divisor, and a quotient (Lesson 3)

$$42 \quad \div \quad 6 \quad = \quad 7$$
↑   ↑   ↑
dividend   divisor   quotient

divisor the number by which the dividend is divided (Lesson 9)

$$\mathbf{4}\overline{)160}$$ with quotient 40
↑
divisor

endpoint a point at the ends of a line segment or a ray (Lesson 19)

equal to (=) a symbol used to show that two numbers have the same value (Lesson 6)

$$191 = 191$$

equation a number sentence with an equal sign (Lessons 1, 2)

$$7 + 3 = y$$

equivalent fractions two or more fractions that name the same value but have different numerators and denominators (Lessons 10, 11, 14)

$$\frac{1}{2} = \frac{2}{4}$$

even number a number that is divisible by 2; even numbers have 0, 2, 4, 6, or 8 in the ones place (Lesson 4)

14

expanded form a way of writing a number that shows the sum of the values of each digit (Lesson 5)

$$6{,}211 = 6{,}000 + 200 + 10 + 1$$

fact family a set of related facts that use the same numbers (Lessons 1, 9)

$$2 \times 3 = 6 \qquad 6 \div 2 = 3$$
$$3 \times 2 = 6 \qquad 6 \div 3 = 2$$

factor a number that is multiplied to get a product (Lesson 1)

$$\underbrace{3 \times 2}_{\text{factors}} = 6$$

factor pair two factors of a number (Lesson 3)

4 × **3** is a factor pair of 12.

figure a geometric shape (Lesson 4)

formula an equation that represents a mathematical relationship (Lesson 17)

$$Area = length \times width$$
$$A = l \times w$$

fraction a part of a whole (Lesson 10)

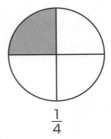

$$\frac{1}{4}$$

greater than (>) a symbol used to show that a number is more than another number (Lesson 6)

$$201 > 199$$

hexagon a two-dimensional figure with 6 sides and 6 angles (Lesson 20)

improper fraction a fraction with a numerator that is greater than or equal to the denominator (Lesson 12)

$$\frac{5}{2}$$

inverse operations operations that undo each other (Lesson 7)

$$18 + 24 = 42$$
$$42 - 24 = 18$$

less than (<) a symbol used to show that a number is smaller than another number (Lesson 6)

$$175 < 180$$

like denominators two or more denominators that are the same (Lesson 12)

$$\frac{1}{5} \qquad \frac{4}{5}$$

line a straight path that goes in two opposite directions without end (Lesson 20)

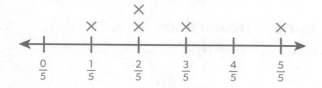

line plot a graph that uses Xs above a number line to record data (Lesson 18)

Ribbon Lengths (in yards)

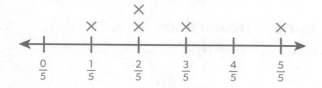

line segment a part of a line with two endpoints (Lesson 20)

mass the amount of matter in an object (Lesson 18)

metric system the system of measurement units most commonly used throughout the world (Lesson 16)

mixed number a number that has a whole number part and a fraction part (Lesson 12)

$$3\frac{1}{5} \leftarrow \text{Fraction part}$$

Whole-number part

multiple the product of a number and another number (Lessons 3, 13)

3, 6, and 9 are multiples of 3.

multiple of 10 the product of 10 and another factor (Lesson 8)

10, 20, 30, 40, and so on are multiples of 10.

multiplication fact a basic fact that has two factors and a product (Lesson 3)

$$2 \quad \times \quad 9 \quad = \quad 18$$

factor   factor   product

number line a line with tic marks that shows equal parts of a whole (Lesson 10)

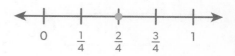

number name a way to show a number in words (Lesson 5)

six thousand, two hundred eleven (6,211)

number pattern a series of numbers that follow a rule (Lesson 4)

pattern: 5, 10, 15, 20, ...

rule: *Add 5.*

numerator the top number in a fraction that tells how many equal parts are being considered (Lessons 10, 11, 18)

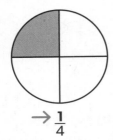

$\rightarrow \frac{1}{4}$

obtuse angle an angle with a measure greater than 90° and less than 180° (Lesson 20)

odd number a whole number that is not divisible by 2; all odd numbers have 1, 3, 5, 7, or 9 in the ones place (Lesson 4)

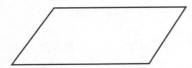

13

parallel lines lines that stay the same distance apart and never meet (Lesson 20)

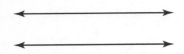

parallelogram a quadrilateral with 2 pairs of opposite sides that are parallel and the same length (Lesson 20)

partial products the numbers you add when parts of numbers are multiplied separately (Lesson 8)

pattern a series of numbers or figures that follows a rule (Lesson 4)

pattern: 2, 4, 8, 16, ...

rule: *Multiply by 2.*

pentagon a two-dimentional figure with 5 sides and 5 angles (Lesson 20)

perimeter the distance around the outside of a closed plane figure (Lesson 17)

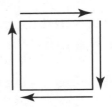

perpendicular lines lines that cross each other at right angles (Lesson 20)

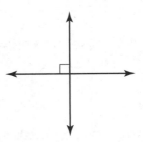

place value the value of a digit based on its position in a number (Lessons 5, 6)

Thousands			Ones		
Hundreds	Tens	Ones	Hundreds	Tens	Ones
		2	7	9	6

point an exact location or position (Lesson 20)

prime number a whole number that has exactly one factor pair, 1 and itself (Lesson 3)

11 is a prime number.

product the answer in a multiplication problem (Lessons 1, 8, 16)

$$3 \times 2 = \mathbf{6}$$
↑
product

protractor a tool for finding the number of degrees in an angle (Lesson 19)

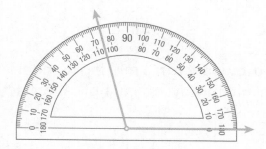

quadrilateral a two-dimensional figure with 4 sides and 4 angles (Lesson 20)

quotient the answer in a division problem (Lessons 1, 9)

quotient
↓
$$4\overline{)160}^{\mathbf{40}}$$

ray a part of a line with an endpoint at one end that goes on forever in the other direction (Lessons 19 and 20)

rectangle a parallelogram with 4 right angles (Lessons 17, 20)

regroup to rename a number a different way (Lesson 2)

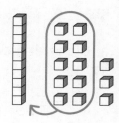

13 ones = 1 ten 3 ones

remainder a number that is left after division has been completed (Lessons 2, 9)

$$12 \div 5 = 2\,R2$$

rhombus a parallelogram with 4 equal sides (Lesson 20)

right angle an angle with a measure of 90° (Lesson 20)

right triangle a triangle with one right angle (Lesson 20)

rule a description of how the terms are related in a pattern (Lesson 4)

rule: *Add 2.*

pattern: 1, 3, 5, 7, ...

shape pattern a series of figures that follow a rule (Lesson 4)

square a rectangle with 4 equal sides (Lessons 17, 20)

square unit a unit used to measure the area of a figure that lies on a flat surface (Lesson 17)

1 cm

standard form a number written using digits (Lesson 5)

6,211

subtract to find how many are left when a quantity is taken away (Lesson 2)

$100 - 25 = 75$

sum the answer in an addition problem (Lessons 12, 16)

$12 + 64 = \mathbf{76}$
↑
sum

term a number in a number pattern (Lesson 4)

pattern: 2, 4, 6, 8, ...

terms: 2, 4, 6, and 8

trapezoid a quadrilateral with 1 pair of parallel sides (Lesson 20)

unit fraction a fraction with 1 as the numerator (Lesson 12)

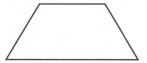

$\frac{1}{10}$ ← 1 in the numerator

unknown factor a missing number you multiply by in a multiplication fact (Lesson 9)

$8 \times \square = 24$

unknown value a number that is missing in a number sentence (Lesson 3)

$36 \div \square = 4$

vertex the point where two rays meet to form an angle (Lesson 19)

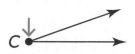

Math Tool: Grouping Mat

Math Tool: Grouping Mat

Math Tool: Grouping Mat

Math Tool: Multiplication Table

×	0	1	2	3	4	5	6	7	8	9	10	11	12
0	0	0	0	0	0	0	0	0	0	0	0	0	0
1	0	1	2	3	4	5	6	7	8	9	10	11	12
2	0	2	4	6	8	10	12	14	16	18	20	22	24
3	0	3	6	9	12	15	18	21	24	27	30	33	36
4	0	4	8	12	16	20	24	28	32	36	40	44	48
5	0	5	10	15	20	25	30	35	40	45	50	55	60
6	0	6	12	18	24	30	36	42	48	54	60	66	72
7	0	7	14	21	28	35	42	49	56	63	70	77	84
8	0	8	16	24	32	40	48	56	64	72	80	88	96
9	0	9	18	27	36	45	54	63	72	81	90	99	108
10	0	10	20	30	40	50	60	70	80	90	100	110	120
11	0	11	22	33	44	55	66	77	88	99	110	121	132
12	0	12	24	36	48	60	72	84	96	108	120	132	144

Math Tool: Counters

Name _____ Date _____

Math Tool: Counters

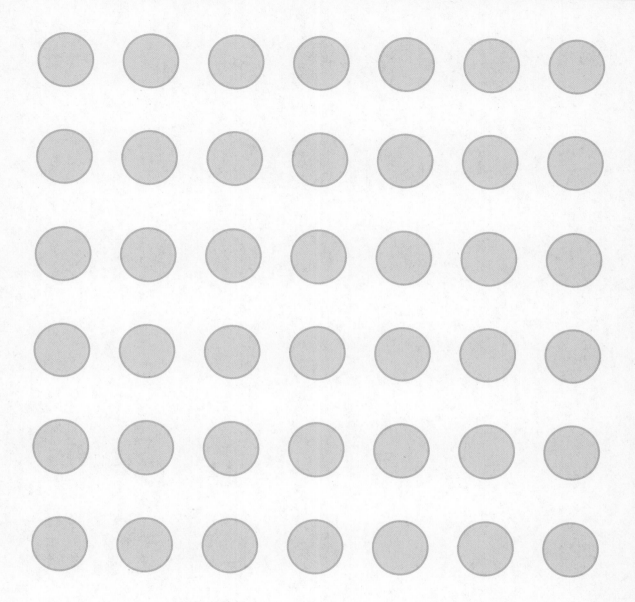

Math Tool: Counters

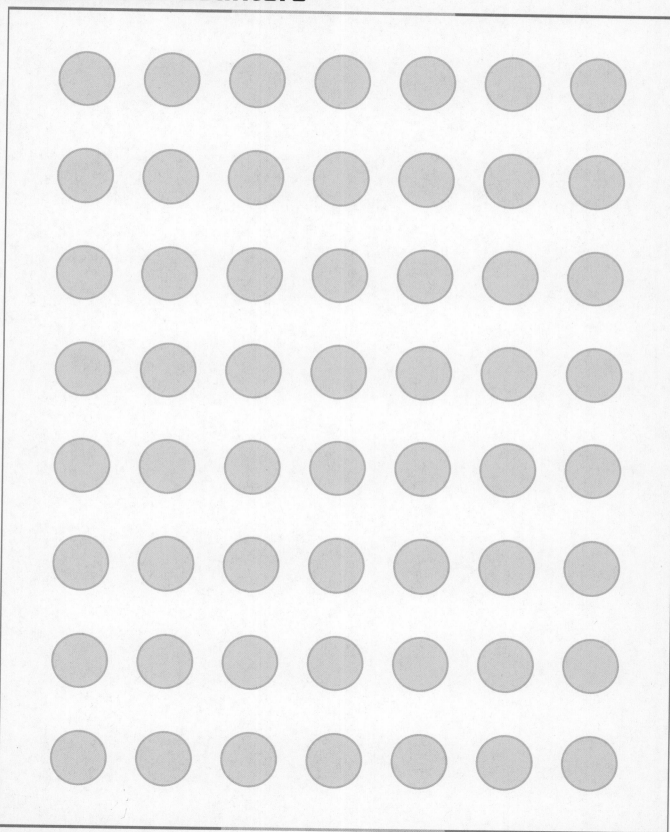

Math Tool: Number Cube

Math Tool: Number Cube

1   2

5

Math Tool: Grid Paper

Name _____ Date _____

Math Tool: Grid Paper

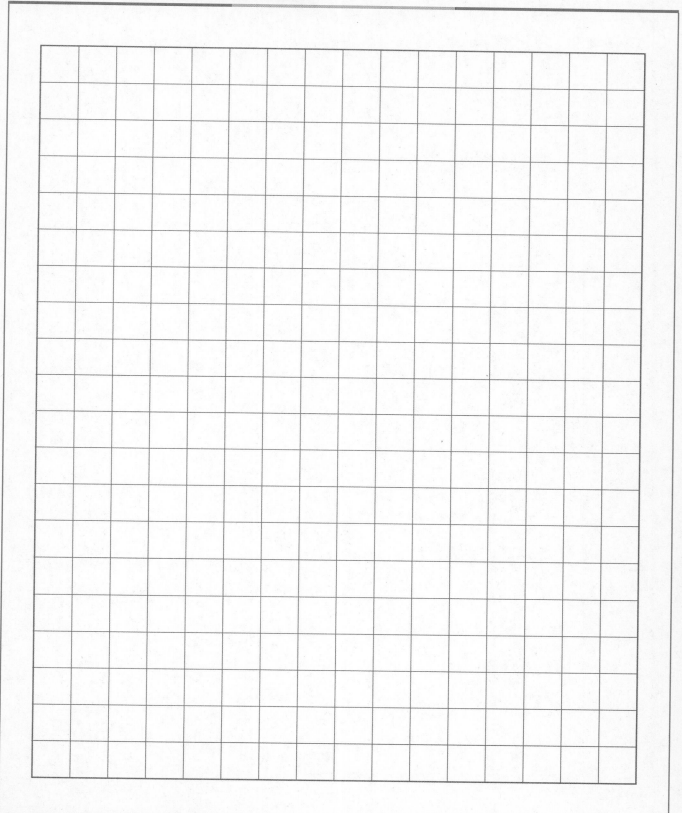

Name _____   Date _____

Math Tool: Grid Paper

Math Tool: Place-Value Charts

Thousands	Hundreds	Tens	Ones

Thousands	Hundreds	Tens	Ones

Thousands	Hundreds	Tens	Ones

Thousands	Hundreds	Tens	Ones

Math Tool: Place-Value Charts

Thousands	Hundreds	Tens	Ones

Thousands	Hundreds	Tens	Ones

Thousands	Hundreds	Tens	Ones

Thousands	Hundreds	Tens	Ones

Math Tool: Area Models

Math Tool: Area Models

Math Tool: Place-Value Models

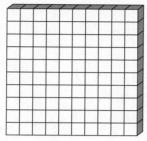

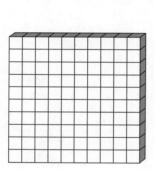

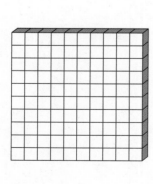

Math Tool: Place-Value Models

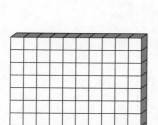

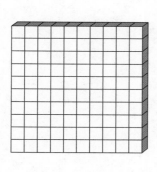

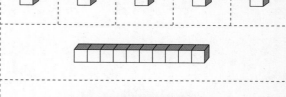

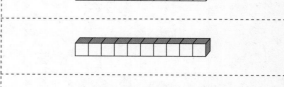

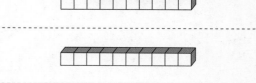

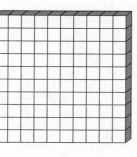

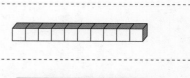

Name _____   Date _____

Math Tool: Place-Value Models

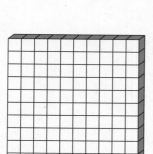

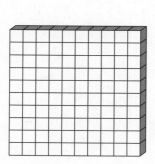
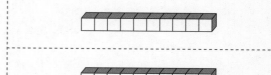
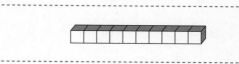
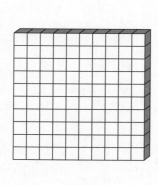
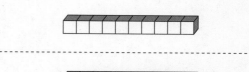
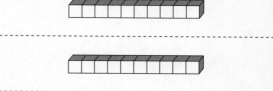

Name _____ Date _____

Math Tool: Fraction Strips

Math Tool: Fraction Strips

Math Tool: Fraction Strips

Math Tool: Fraction Strips

Math Tool: Labeled Fraction Strips

1

$\frac{1}{2}$	$\frac{1}{2}$

$\frac{1}{3}$	$\frac{1}{3}$	$\frac{1}{3}$

$\frac{1}{4}$	$\frac{1}{4}$	$\frac{1}{4}$	$\frac{1}{4}$

$\frac{1}{5}$	$\frac{1}{5}$	$\frac{1}{5}$	$\frac{1}{5}$	$\frac{1}{5}$

$\frac{1}{6}$	$\frac{1}{6}$	$\frac{1}{6}$	$\frac{1}{6}$	$\frac{1}{6}$	$\frac{1}{6}$

$\frac{1}{8}$	$\frac{1}{8}$	$\frac{1}{8}$	$\frac{1}{8}$	$\frac{1}{8}$	$\frac{1}{8}$	$\frac{1}{8}$	$\frac{1}{8}$

$\frac{1}{10}$	$\frac{1}{10}$	$\frac{1}{10}$	$\frac{1}{10}$	$\frac{1}{10}$	$\frac{1}{10}$	$\frac{1}{10}$	$\frac{1}{10}$	$\frac{1}{10}$	$\frac{1}{10}$

$\frac{1}{12}$	$\frac{1}{12}$	$\frac{1}{12}$	$\frac{1}{12}$	$\frac{1}{12}$	$\frac{1}{12}$	$\frac{1}{12}$	$\frac{1}{12}$	$\frac{1}{12}$	$\frac{1}{12}$	$\frac{1}{12}$	$\frac{1}{12}$

Math Tool: Labeled Fraction Strips

1

$\frac{1}{2}$	$\frac{1}{2}$

$\frac{1}{3}$	$\frac{1}{3}$	$\frac{1}{3}$

$\frac{1}{4}$	$\frac{1}{4}$	$\frac{1}{4}$	$\frac{1}{4}$

$\frac{1}{5}$	$\frac{1}{5}$	$\frac{1}{5}$	$\frac{1}{5}$	$\frac{1}{5}$

$\frac{1}{6}$	$\frac{1}{6}$	$\frac{1}{6}$	$\frac{1}{6}$	$\frac{1}{6}$	$\frac{1}{6}$

$\frac{1}{8}$	$\frac{1}{8}$	$\frac{1}{8}$	$\frac{1}{8}$	$\frac{1}{8}$	$\frac{1}{8}$	$\frac{1}{8}$	$\frac{1}{8}$

$\frac{1}{10}$	$\frac{1}{10}$	$\frac{1}{10}$	$\frac{1}{10}$	$\frac{1}{10}$	$\frac{1}{10}$	$\frac{1}{10}$	$\frac{1}{10}$	$\frac{1}{10}$	$\frac{1}{10}$

$\frac{1}{12}$	$\frac{1}{12}$	$\frac{1}{12}$	$\frac{1}{12}$	$\frac{1}{12}$	$\frac{1}{12}$	$\frac{1}{12}$	$\frac{1}{12}$	$\frac{1}{12}$	$\frac{1}{12}$	$\frac{1}{12}$	$\frac{1}{12}$

Math Tool: Labeled Fraction Strips

1

$\frac{1}{2}$	$\frac{1}{2}$

$\frac{1}{3}$	$\frac{1}{3}$	$\frac{1}{3}$

$\frac{1}{4}$	$\frac{1}{4}$	$\frac{1}{4}$	$\frac{1}{4}$

$\frac{1}{5}$	$\frac{1}{5}$	$\frac{1}{5}$	$\frac{1}{5}$	$\frac{1}{5}$

$\frac{1}{6}$	$\frac{1}{6}$	$\frac{1}{6}$	$\frac{1}{6}$	$\frac{1}{6}$	$\frac{1}{6}$

$\frac{1}{8}$	$\frac{1}{8}$	$\frac{1}{8}$	$\frac{1}{8}$	$\frac{1}{8}$	$\frac{1}{8}$	$\frac{1}{8}$	$\frac{1}{8}$

$\frac{1}{10}$	$\frac{1}{10}$	$\frac{1}{10}$	$\frac{1}{10}$	$\frac{1}{10}$	$\frac{1}{10}$	$\frac{1}{10}$	$\frac{1}{10}$	$\frac{1}{10}$	$\frac{1}{10}$

$\frac{1}{12}$	$\frac{1}{12}$	$\frac{1}{12}$	$\frac{1}{12}$	$\frac{1}{12}$	$\frac{1}{12}$	$\frac{1}{12}$	$\frac{1}{12}$	$\frac{1}{12}$	$\frac{1}{12}$	$\frac{1}{12}$	$\frac{1}{12}$

Name _____ Date _____

Math Tool: Grids

 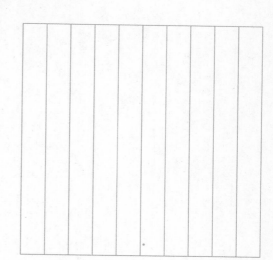

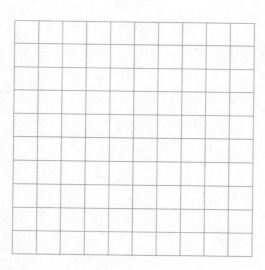 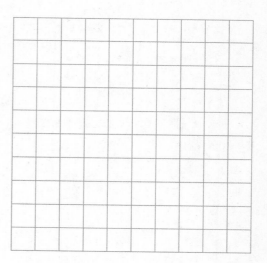

Math Tool: Customary Units

Equivalent Measures of Length

1 foot (ft) = 12 inches (in.)

1 yard (yd) = 3 feet

1 yard = 36 inches

Equivalent Measures of Weight

1 pound (lb) = 16 ounces (oz)

Equivalent Measures of Capacity

1 gallon (gal) = 4 quarts (qt)

1 quart = 2 pints (pt)

1 pint = 2 cups (c)

Equivalent Measures of Time

1 hour (hr) = 60 minutes (min)

1 minute = 60 seconds (sec)

Math Tool: Metric Units

Equivalent Measures of Length
1 kilometer (km) = 1,000 meters (m)
1 meter = 100 centimeters (cm)

Equivalent Measures of Mass
1 kilogram (kg) = 1,000 grams (g)

Equivalent Measures of Capacity
1 liter (L) = 1,000 milliliters (mL)

Name _____ Date _____

Math Tool: 360° Circle

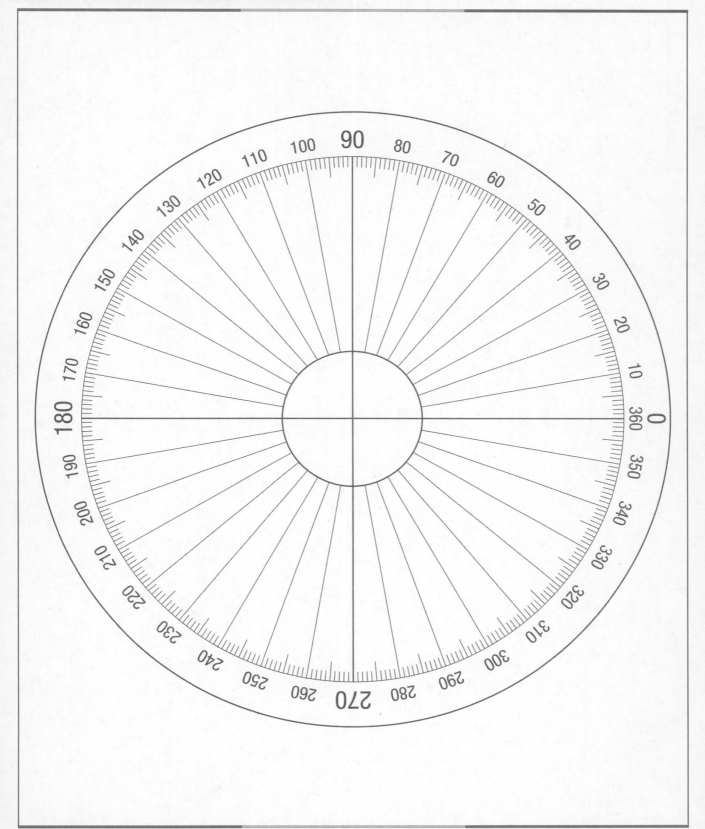

Math Tool: Two-Dimensional Figures

circle
0 sides
0 angles

oval
0 sides
0 angles

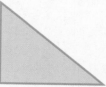

triangle
3 sides
3 angles

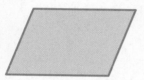

parallelogram
4 sides
4 angles

square
4 equal sides
4 right angles

rectangle
4 sides
4 right angles

rhombus
4 equal sides
4 angles

trapezoid
4 sides
4 angles

pentagon
5 sides
5 angles

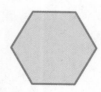

hexagon
6 sides
6 angles

octagon
8 sides
8 angles